NEW 2018

by ARGO

COMMON CORE ENGLISH

GRADE 5

PART I: MULTIPLE CHOICE

Visit **www.argoprep.com** to get
FREE access to our online platform.

1000+ Minutes of Video Explanations and more!

Authors: Jill Mountain
                  Anayet Chowdhury
                  Eduard Suleyman
                  Vladislav Suleyman

Design: Vladislav Suleyman

At Argo Brothers, we are dedicated to providing quality and effective sup-plemental practice for your child. We would love to hear your honest feed-back and **review** of our workbooks on **Amazon**.

Argo Brothers is one of the leading providers of supplemental educational products and services. We offer affordable and effective test prep solutions to educators, parents and students. Learning should be fun and easy! For that reason, most of our workbooks come with detailed video answer explanations taught by one of our fabulous instructors. Our goal is to make your life easier, so let us know how we can help you by e-mailing us at **info@argobrothers.com**

OTHER BOOKS BY ARGO BROTHERS

Here are some other test prep workbooks by Argo Brothers you may be interested in. All of our workbooks come equipped with detailed video explanations to make your learning experience a breeze! Subscribe to our mailing list at www.argobrothers.com to receive custom updates about your education.

GRADE 2

GRADE 3

GRADE 4

GRADE 5

GRADE 6

GRADE 7

GRADE 4

GRADE 5

TABLE OF CONTENTS

HOW TO USE THE BOOK

This workbook is designed to give lots of practice with the English Common Core State Standards (CCSS). By practicing and mastering this entire workbook, your child will become very familiar and comfortable with the state english exam. If you are a teacher using this workbook for your student's, you will notice each question is labeled with the specific standard so you can easily assign your students problems in the workbook. This workbook takes the CCSS and divides them up among 20 weeks. By working on these problems on a daily basis, students will be able to (1) find any deficiencies in their understanding and/or practice of english and (2) have small successes each day that will build proficiency and confidence in their abilities.

You can find detailed video explanations to each problem in the book by visiting:
www.argoprep.com

We strongly recommend watching the videos as it will reinforce the fundamental concepts. Please note, scrap paper may be necessary while using this workbook so that the student has sufficient space to show their work.

For a detailed overview of the Common Core State Standards for 5th grade, please visit:
www.corestandards.org/ELA-Literacy/L/5/

For more practice with 5th Grade English, be sure to check out our other book:
Argo Brothers English Workbook, Grade 5: Common Core **Free Response**

WEEK 1

VIDEO
EXPLANATIONS

ARGOPREP.COM

Excerpt from **Black Beauty** *by Anna Sewell*

When I was four years old Squire Gordon came to look at me. He examined my eyes, my mouth, and my legs; he felt them all down; and then I had to walk and trot and gallop before him. He seemed to like me, and said, "When he has been well broken in he will do very well." My master said he would break me in himself, as he should not like me to be frightened or hurt, and he lost no time about it, for the next day he began.

Every one may not know what breaking in is, therefore I will describe it. It means to teach a horse to wear a saddle and bridle, and to carry on his back a man, woman or child; to go just the way they wish, and to go quietly. Besides this he has to learn to wear a collar, a crupper, and a breeching, and to stand still while they are put on; then to have a cart or a chaise fixed behind, so that he cannot walk or trot without dragging it after him; and he must go fast or slow, just as his driver wishes. He must never start at what he sees, nor speak to other horses, nor bite, nor kick, nor have any will of his own; but always do his master's will, even though he may be very tired or hungry; but the worst of all is, when his harness is once on, he may neither jump for joy nor lie down for weariness. So you see this breaking in is a great thing.

I had of course long been used to a halter and a headstall, and to be led about in the fields and lanes quietly, but now I was to have a bit and bridle; my master gave me some oats as usual, and after a good deal of coaxing he got the bit into my mouth, and the bridle fixed, but it was a nasty thing! Those who have never had a bit in their mouths cannot think how bad it feels; a great piece of cold hard steel as thick as a man's finger to be pushed into one's mouth, between one's teeth, and over one's tongue, with the ends coming out at the corner of your mouth, and held fast there by straps over your head, under your throat, round your nose, and under your chin; so that no way in the world can you get rid of the nasty hard thing; it is very bad! yes, very bad! at least I thought so; but I knew my mother always wore one when she went out, and all horses did when they were grown up; and so, what with the nice oats, and what with my master's pats, kind words, and gentle ways, I got to wear my bit and bridle.

Read the questions before you read the passage. As you read the passage, highlight or underline information related to one of the questions.

Exercises

1. Which statement best reflects how the narrator feels about wearing the bit?

A. He hates it and wishes he didn't have to wear it.
B. He sees it as a sign that he is becoming an adult
C. He resents his master for making him wear it.
D. He likes it because it makes him feel very important.

RL.5.6

2. Which excerpt from the text best supports how the narrator feels about wearing the bit?

A. "Those who have never had a bit in their mouths cannot think how bad it feels..."
B. "It is very bad! Yes, very bad! At least I thought so; but I knew my mother always wore one when she went out, and all horses did when they were grown up.."
C. "...but now I was to have a bit and bridle, my master gave me some oats as usual, and after a good deal of coaxing he got the bit into my mouth..."
D. "He must never start at what he sees, nor speak to other horses, nor bite, nor kick..."

RL.5.5

3. What does the narrator mean when he says, "So you see this breaking in is a great thing," at the end of the second paragraph?

A. He means that breaking in a horse is wonderful.
B. He means that it is important that a horse be broken in correctly.
C. He means that breaking in a horse is a complicated process.
D. He means that being broken in makes a horse feel good about himself.

RL.5.4

4. What is suggested by this line from the last paragraph: "Those who have never had a bit in their mouths cannot think of how bad it feels..."

A. The narrator is a horse and he imagines some of his readers are horses as well.
B. The narrator is a person who has broken in many horses.
C. The narrator is person writing about something that he feels strongly about.
D. The narrator is a horse and is an expert on this topic.

RL.5.2

5. In paragraph 2, what does the narrator mean when he says, "He must never start at what he sees..."

A. A horse cannot start walking or running until his rider tells him to do so.
B. The horse cannot begin his training until his master determines it is okay.
C. A horse must always be calm, no matter what he sees.
D. A well-trained horse doesn't ask questions; he just does as he is told.

RL.5.4

6. How does the second paragraph contribute to the development of the story?

A. It explains the skills a trainer needs to "break in" a horse.
B. It shows that the narrator understands and accepts his training.
C. It describes the narrator's behaviors that will interfere with his training.
D. It shows that the narrator is reluctant to be trained.

RL.5.1

The Old Brown Horse *W.F. Holmes*

The old brown horse looks over the fence
In a weary sort of way.
He seems to be saying to all who pass:
"Well, folks, I've had my day-
I'm simply watching the world go by,   (5)
And nobody seems to mind,
As they're dashing past in their motor-cars,
A horse who is lame and half-blind."
The old brown horse has a shaggy coat,
But once he was young and trim,   (10)
And he used to trot through the woods and lanes
With the man who was fond of him.
But his master rides in a motor-car,
And it makes him feel quite sad
When he thinks of the days that used to be,   (15)
And of all the times they had.
Sometimes a friendly soul will stop
Near the fence, where the tired old head
Rests wearily on the topmost bar,
And a friendly word is said.   (20)
Then the old brown horse gives a little sigh
As he feels the kindly touch
Of a hand on his mane or his shaggy coat,
And he doesn't mind so much.

So if you pass by the field one day,   (25)
Just stop for a word or two
With the old brown horse who was once as young
And as full of life as you.
He'll love the touch of your soft young hand,
And I know he'll seem to say   (30)
"Oh, thank you, friend, for the kindly thought
For a horse who has had his day."

When reading poetry, be sure to read according to the punctuation the poet has used. Don't end each thought at the end of each line; continue reading until you reach a period or semicolon, which tells you the thought is complete.

Exercises

1. What technique does the speaker use to suggest what the horse is feeling?

  A. The speaker describes how people react to the horse.
  B. The speaker compares the horse to a car to show that the horse has been replaced.
  C. The speaker imagines what the horse might say.
  D. The speaker shares the horse's words and feelings.

RL.5.6

4. Which statement best describes the theme of this poem?

  A. All animals deserve care and respect.
  B. It is important to honor those left behind by progress.
  C. It doesn't take a lot of effort to be kind.
  D. Kindness is more important than progress.

RL.5.2

2. What shift occurs in the second stanza of the poem?

  A. The speaker addresses the reader directly.
  B. The speaker looks to the horse's future.
  C. The speaker moves from speaking about the horse in a general sense to speaking about him in specific details.
  D. The speaker considers the horse's owner's point of view.

RL.5.5

5. What is the best definition of the word "lame" as it is used in line 8?

  A. Uninspiring and dull
  B. Not convincing
  C. Sad and pathetic
  D. Limping or handicapped

RL.5.4

3. Review lines 31-32. What does the phrase "has had his day" most likely mean?

  A. The horse has been standing at the fence all day.
  B. The horse has had a very good day so far.
  C. The horse's best experiences are in the past.
  D. The horse is looking for someone to help him have a better life.

RL.5.4

6. How does the horse feel as he watches cars pass by on the road?

  A. Resentful of all the people who have chosen to drive cars instead of ride horses.
  B. Hopeful that someone will stop and pay attention to him.
  C. Nostalgic for the days when he was considered useful.
  D. Anxious about what will happen to him now that he is no longer useful.

RL.5.1

Man vs Horse – A Story of Evolution

(1) Every June, in the town of Llanwrtyd Wells, Wales, hundreds of runners and horseback riders compete in the Man versus Horse Marathon. People might assume the winner would always be the horse, but that is not the case. Humans have won the race several times. It is not so far-fetched to imagine a human runner outlasting a horse in a long-distance race. Research on the development of human physiology has revealed that the human body has evolved to be an efficient long-distance running machine. It is specially designed to outlast most four-legged animals.

(2) Humans evolved this way in order to survive. Prehistoric humans traveled twenty miles or more, on foot, every day in search of food. In the time before projectile weapons, or weapons like spears, humans needed to get very close to their prey in order to kill them. Usually, prey like antelope and deer can move much more quickly than humans over short distances. However, if the human hunters could force the prey to run longer distances, the animals would become exhausted. That gave prehistoric hunters an advantage. Humans who could endure the long-distance chase necessary for a successful hunt were the humans who ate and had food to share. They were the humans who started families and became ancestors to all of us.

(3) There are several physical characteristics that make humans great long-distance runners. First, unlike other animals, humans cool their overheated bodies by perspiring. Quadrupeds, like horses, deer, or antelope, do not perspire. They cool their bodies by panting. Panting only cools the blood vessels in the head and neck. The act of panting requires additional energy. An animal becomes even more tired by panting.

(4) Perspiration, on the other hand, is a passive function. It takes no energy from the human body. As the human body overheats, sweat glands, which are located in different parts of the body to most efficiently cool major organs and body systems, begin to excrete moisture. As this moisture evaporates, the body is cooled. A human runner may sweat profusely. This advanced human-cooling evolution means that humans can run much longer distances than many other animals without overheating.

(5) Humans' feet and legs have developed to support the most efficient use of energy in long-distance running. The fact that a human's big toe is straight and aligned with the other toes, unlike the big toe of, for example, a great ape, which is off to the side, means it takes less energy for a human to run than it does for an ape. The big toe also helps a human runner push off to spring from a stand-still quickly, and without expelling a lot of energy.

(6) Finally, the human upper body, with a narrow waist and long arms that swing easily in straight arcs helps the human runner maintain an even gait and stay on a path without wild, energy-burning divergences or movements from side to side.

(7) Although success as a long-distance runner is no longer required to survive, running is still a very popular sport. Many cultures still consider the body shape associated with running to be physically attractive and a sign of good health.

In informational texts the main idea of the passage is often included in the introduction. After reading, think about how the details in the text support the main point the author is making.

Exercises

1. What is the advantage in perspiring rather than panting to cool the body?

RI.5.2

2. How did hunting likely change with the invention of projectile weapons?

RI.5.3

3. Which metaphor from paragraph 1 makes a comparison to show how humans' physical characteristics have made them excellent long-distance runners?

A. People might assume the winner would always be the horse, but that is not the case.
B. Research on the development of human physiology has revealed that the human body has evolved to be an efficient long-distance running machine.
C. It is specially designed to outlast most four-legged animals.
D. ... hundreds of runners and horseback riders compete in the Man versus Horse Marathon.

RI.5.4

5. Which statement is supported by the last paragraph of this passage?

A. Prehistoric preference for a body evolved for long distance running has translated into modern-day ideas of what makes a person attractive.
B. Because people no longer have to be strong long-distance runners to survive, few modern people have the body shape associated with running.
C. Different cultures have different standards for what makes a person physically attractive.
D. Modern-day long distance runners tend to be more successful than those who do not have the physical traits of runners.

RI.5.1

4. According to the passage, what is the advantage of having long arms and a narrow waist?

A. Humans with long arms and a narrow waist can run along a straight path, rather that burn energy running erratically.
B. The humans' narrow waist waists distribute energy more efficiently between the trunk and the legs.
C. The humans' long, swinging arms provide air currents to hasten evaporation and make the cooling of perspiration more efficient.
D. By bending at the waist and swinging their arms humans are able to spring into motion and start running more quickly.

RI.5.8

6. Based on paragraph 3, the reader can infer that which of these is a drawback of using panting to cool the body?

A. Since panting only cools the major organs, smaller, yet important organs, such as the appendix, are not cooled.
B. Panting is never a superior body-cooling function.
C. While panting cools the brain, it does not effectively cool other major organs such as the heart and lungs.
D. Panting is an evolved trait that only benefits long-distance runners.

RI.5.2

WEEK 2

VIDEO
EXPLANATIONS

ARGOPREP.COM

From **Anne of Green Gables** *by Lucy Maud Montgomery*

(http://www.online-literature.com/lucy_montgomery/anne_green_gables/1/)

There are plenty of people in Avonlea. There are also a lot of people who pay a lot of attention to what everyone else is doing, but don't pay enough attention to their own lives. Mrs. Rachel Lynde was one of those capable people who could do both. She could manage her own concerns and those of other folks too. She was a notable housewife; her work was always done and well done; she ran the Sewing Circle. She helped run the Sunday-school. She was the strongest prop of the Church Aid Society and Foreign Missions Auxiliary. Yet with all this Mrs. Rachel found abundant time to sit for hours at her kitchen window, knitting "cotton warp" quilts--she had knitted sixteen of them, as Avonlea housekeepers were wont to tell in awed voices-- and keeping a sharp eye on the main road that crossed the hollow and wound up the steep red hill beyond. She was always on the lookout for what other people were up to. Since Avonlea occupied a little triangular peninsula jutting out into the Gulf of St. Lawrence with water on two sides of it, anybody who went into to town or out of town had to pass over that hill road and go right by Mrs. Rachel's all-seeing eyes. No one could escape her inspection.

She was sitting there one afternoon in early June. The sun was coming in at the window warm and bright. The orchard on the slope below the house was like a blushing bride. The pinky- white blooms of the apple trees were hummed over by a myriad of bees. Thomas Lynde-- a meek little man whom Avonlea people called "Rachel Lynde's husband"--was sowing his late turnip seed on the hill field beyond the barn. Matthew Cuthbert ought to have been sowing his on the big red brook field away over by Green Gables. Mrs. Rachel knew that he was supposed to planting his turnip seeds because she had heard him tell Peter Morrison the evening before in William J. Blair's store over at Carmody that he meant to sow his turnip seed the next afternoon. Peter had asked him what he was up to, of course. Matthew Cuthbert had never been known to volunteer information about anything in his whole life. He was a private man, and if Peter hadn't brought up planting with direct questions, Mrs. Rachel would never have known that Matthew Cuthbert was, most definitely, not doing what he was supposed to be doing that afternoon in early June.

An author tells us about a character in many ways: what the character says, what she does, what she thinks, and how others react to her. As you read about a character, work to put together all the information the author provides.

Exercises

1. Which excerpt from the text best supports the claim that Mrs. Lynde is nosy.

    A. There are also a lot of people who pay a lot of attention to what everyone else is doing, but don't pay enough attention to their own lives.
    B. She helped run the Sunday-school. She was the strongest prop of the Church Aid Society and Foreign Missions Auxiliary.
    C. She was always on the lookout for what other people were up to.
    D. Matthew Cuthbert ought to have been sowing his on the big red brook field away over by Green Gables.

RL.5.1

2. Which statement best contrasts Thomas Lynde and Mathew Cuthbert?

    A. Thomas Lynde is meek, while Matthew Cuthbert is more likely to talk to other people.
    B. Matthew Cuthbert is friends with Peter Morrison, but Thomas Lynde is not.
    C. Thomas Lynde planned to plant turnips, but Matthew Cuthbert did not.
    D. Matthew Cuthbert was not planting turnips that day, but Thomas Lynde was

RL.5.3

3. What does the expression "keeping a sharp eye" mean as it is used in this passage?

    A. Stare in to the sun.
    B. Be critical of everyone she sees.
    C. Watch closely.
    D. Work diligently.

RL.5.4

4. The narrator of this passage can best be described as...

    A. Gently critical of Mrs. Lynde
    B. Afraid of Mrs. Lynde
    C. Impressed by Mrs. Lynde
    D. Sympathetic to Mrs. Lynde

RL.5.6

5. Review this excerpt from the text:

"... she ran the Sewing Circle. She helped run the Sunday-school." Which definition of "run" is used in this text?

    A. To move quickly
    B. To chase
    C. A quick visit or errand
    D. To manage

RL.5.4

6. Which excerpt from the text gives the reader an impression of the relationship between Mr. Lynde and Mrs. Lynde?

    A. Matthew Cuthbert ought to have been sowing his on the big red brook field away over by Green Gables.
    B. Thomas Lynde-- a meek little man whom Avonlea people called "Rachel Lynde's husband"--was sowing his late turnip seed on the hill field beyond the barn.
    C. The orchard on the slope below the house was like a blushing bride. The pinky- white blooms of the apple trees were hummed over by a myriad of bees.
    D. Matthew Cuthbert was, most definitely, not doing what he was supposed to be doing that afternoon in early June.

RL.5.2

The Art of Public Speaking *by Dale Carnegie*

(https://www.gutenberg.org/files/16317/16317-h/16317-h.htm#CHAPTER_X)

When traveling through the Northwest some time ago, a friend of mine was strolling along a street after dinner. He noticed a crowd listening to a man speaking on a corner. My friend remembered advice he'd received, that he could learn something from everyone he met. So, he stopped to listen to the man's speech. The man was selling a hair tonic, which he claimed to have discovered in Arizona. He removed his hat to show what this remedy had done for him. His thick dark hair shone in the light. It was oiled and impressive. He washed his face in it to demonstrate that it was as harmless as water. He talked and talked and all the people listening were excited. Soon, the man was awash in a wave of green, as people started throwing money at him. They were eager to get a bottle of his tonic.

When the man had supplied the audience with hair tonic, he asked, "Why do you think there are more bald men than women?" No one knew. He explained, "It is because women wear thinner soled shoes! They are more closely connected to earth... through natural electricity!" He continued, "You see, men wear thick soled shoes, and they don't make a good connection with earth, so, the earth's electricity doesn't move through them. Without that electrical food, men can't grow hair!"

Of course my friend didn't believe this foolishness, but he could tell that many of the people standing on the street were fascinated. The man went on and said, "The solution, men, is to attach a small copper plate to the bottom of your shoe. That copper plate my friends... that is what stands between you and a full head of hair."

Of course the man was selling the solution to this problem —a little copper plate to be nailed on the bottom of the shoe. He described in enthusiastic and vivid terms the desirability of escaping baldness—and explained how his copper plates provided the protection people wanted. Strange as it may seem when the story is told in cold print, the speaker's enthusiasm had swept his audience with him. People crushed around his stand with outstretched hands full of cash, almost begging him to sell them these copper plates!

And this is the wonderful, persuasive power of enthusiasm!

Enthusiasm sent Columbus and three small ships plying the unknown sea to the shores of a new world. When Napoleon's army were worn out and discouraged in their ascent of the Alps, the Little Corporal stopped them and ordered the bands to play music. Under its soul-stirring strains there were no Alps.

Ralph Waldo Emerson once said said: "Nothing great was ever achieved without enthusiasm." Thomas Carlyle declared that "Every great movement in history has been the triumph of enthusiasm." It is as contagious as a disease. It isn't enough to be a good speaker. You must sweep your audience with you in a pulsation of enthusiasm. Let yourself go.

How are we to acquire and develop enthusiasm?

It is not to be slipped on like a jacket. You can't learn to be enthusiastic by reading a book. It is a growth— an effect. Enthusiasm is felt in the soul. To be enthusiastic you must truly believe in what you're saying.

When reading a non-fiction essay like this, pause at the end of every paragraph. In your mind summarize the paragraph and think about how it is related to the main point.

Exercises

1. This passage has two main parts. The purpose of first part of the passage is to...

   A. Provide an example of the power of enthusiasm.
   B. Warn readers about dishonest salespeople they might encounter on a street.
   C. Demonstrate how the narrator's friend was easily fooled by a tricky salesman.
   D. Explain how a speaker can become enthusiastic, and therefore, more convincing.

   RI.5.5

2. Which sentence from the text best supports the idea that the man selling the copper plates was successful only because he was an enthusiastic speaker?

   A. Soon, the man was awash in a wave of green, as people started throwing money at him.
   B. Strange as it may seem when the story is told in cold print, the speaker's enthusiasm had swept his audience with him.
   C. The man was selling a hair tonic, which he claimed to have discovered in Arizona.
   D. And this is the wonderful, persuasive power of enthusiasm!

   RI.5.8

3. Based on the main point of this passage, which statement about the salesman must be true?

   A. The salesman knows the products he's selling are useless.
   B. The salesman is suspicious of other people.
   C. The salesman is very wealthy.
   D. The salesman believes what he tells people about his products.

   RI.5.2

4. Which example from the text best supports the claim that "Nothing great was ever achieved without enthusiasm?"

   A. The salesman's success in selling copper plates.
   B. The narrator's belief that enthusiasm cannot be learned.
   C. The example of Columbus sailing for the new world.
   D. The quote from Thomas Carlyle.

   RI.5.8

5. Review the sentence below from the passage. Which definition of "cold" best fits how the word is used in this context:

   "Strange as it may seem when the story is told in cold print, the speaker's enthusiasm had swept his audience with him."

   A. At a low temperature
   B. Unfriendly
   C. Without emotion
   D. Rude

   RI.5.4

6. Read the following excerpt from the text. Which is the best synonym for "crushed" as it is used here?

   "People crushed around his stand with outstretched hands full of cash..."

   A. Puppy love or infatuation
   B. Defeated
   C. Thronged
   D. Humiliated

   RI.5.4

From **Hero Tales from American History** *by Henry Cabot Lodge and Theodore Roosevelt*

(https://www.gutenberg.org/files/1864/1864-h/1864-h.htm)

(1)   George Washington was born in the days when the American colonies were ruled by British aristocrats, or wealthy Englishmen of high social standing. Young George was born into a respectable family who had a long tradition of living in the colonies. People in the area thought highly of the Washingtons. But, other than the good reputation of his family, which he lived up to, George Washington had little. His family was poor; his mother was left early a widow, and he was forced after a very limited education to go out into the world to fight for himself. Luckily he was a very adventurous young man. He became a surveyor, or a person who measures the boundaries of plots of land before they are bought or sold. In the days before much of the United States was settled, his work required him to venture into the wilderness, where he soon grew to be an expert hunter and backwoodsman.

(2)   Even as a boy the seriousness of George's character and his mental and physical strength were noticed by those about him. Responsibility and military command were put in his hands at an age when most young men are just leaving college. As the times grew threatening on the frontier, he was sent on a perilous mission to the Indians, in which, after passing through many hardships and dangers, he achieved success. When the troubles came with France it was by the soldiers under his command that the first shots were fired in the war which was to determine whether the North American continent should be French or English. He served with distinction all through the French war, and when peace came he went back to the estate which he had inherited from his brother, the most admired man in Virginia.

(3)   At that time he married, and during the ensuing years he lived the life of a Virginia planter, successful in his private affairs and serving the public effectively but quietly as a member of the House of Burgesses. When the troubles with the mother country began to thicken he was slow to take extreme ground, but he never wavered in his belief that all attempts to oppress the colonies should be resisted. When he once took up his position there was no shadow of turning. He was one of Virginia's delegates to the first Continental Congress, and, although he said but little, he was regarded by all the representatives from the other colonies as the strongest man among them. There was something about him even then which commanded the respect and the confidence of every one who came in contact with him.

(4)   It was from New England, far removed from his own State, that the demand came for his appointment as commander-in-chief of the American army. Silently he accepted the duty, and, leaving Philadelphia, took command of the army at Cambridge, Massachusetts. There is no need to trace him through the events that followed. From the time when he drew his sword under the famous elm tree, he was the embodiment of the American Revolution, and without him that revolution would have failed almost at the start. How he carried it to victory through defeat and trial and every possible obstacle is known to all Americans.

TIP of the **DAY**

Pay attention to how nonfiction texts are organized. Some present facts in time order, or chronologically; some use cause and effect or problem and solution. Some use a combination of strategies. Knowing how the text is organized makes it easier to understand how ideas are related.

Exercises

1. How does the author support his claim that George Washington was frequently motivated to great achievements by hardships or crises? Use evidence from the text to support your response.

_____

_____

_____

_____

_____

_____

_____

_____

_____

_____

RI.5.1

2. Read the following excerpt from the text, "There was something about him even then which commanded the respect and the confidence of every one who came in contact with him." According to this author, what aspects of Washington's character led to others respecting him?

_____

_____

_____

_____

_____

_____

_____

_____

_____

RI.5.3

3. Which statement best summarizes the main point of paragraph 3.

A. Washington earned his reputation by being fast to act against tyranny and by loudly stating his position in public.
B. Washington was a quiet man who opposed tyranny and held strong to his beliefs no matter what challenges he faced.
C. Washington proved that he was stronger than other men and, as a result, was put in a position of leadership.
D. Washington was reluctant to play a role in politics, and did not want to become involved in a conflict.

RI.5.2

4. Which statement best describes how this text is organized?

A. It is organized using cause and effect, to show how national and political events effected George Washington's life and career.
B. It is organized using problem and solution, demonstrating how George Washington addressed and solved problems in the American colonies.
C. It is organized by order of importance, focusing on the most important or memorable events in Washington's life earlier in the passage, then covering the less important events.
D. It is organized in chronological order, providing an overview of important events in Washington's life in time order, starting when he was a child and progressing through his adulthood.

RI.5.5

5. From what type of book is this text most likely excerpted?

A. Realistic fiction
B. Personal essay
C. Biography
D. Autobiography

RI.5.10

6. According to the text, what was an effect of Washington's family's financial situation when he was very young?

A. He was well respected by his men.
B. He had limited formal education.
C. He inherited a large estate.
D. He became a soldier.

RI.5.5

WEEK 3

VIDEO
EXPLANATIONS

ARGOPREP.COM

From **The Wonderful Wizard of Oz** *by L. Frank Baum*

(http://www.gutenberg.org/ebooks/55)

(1)   Dorothy lived in the midst of the great Kansas prairies, with Uncle Henry, who was a farmer, and Aunt Em, who was the farmer's wife. Their house was small, for the lumber to build it had to be carried by wagon many miles. There were four walls, a floor and a roof, which made one room; and this room contained a rusty looking cookstove, a cupboard for the dishes, a table, three or four chairs, and the beds. Uncle Henry and Aunt Em had a big bed in one corner, and Dorothy a little bed in another corner. There was no garret at all, and no cellar--except a small hole dug in the ground, called a cyclone cellar, where the family could go in case one of those great whirlwinds arose, mighty enough to crush any building in its path. It was reached by a trap door in the middle of the floor, from which a ladder led down into the small, dark hole.

(2)   When Dorothy stood in the doorway and looked around, she could see nothing but the great gray prairie on every side. Not a tree nor a house broke the broad sweep of flat country that reached to the edge of the sky in all directions. The sun had baked the plowed land into a gray mass, with little cracks running through it. Even the grass was not green, for the sun had burned the tops of the long blades until they were the same gray color to be seen everywhere. Once the house had been painted, but the sun blistered the paint and the rains washed it away, and now the house was as dull and gray as everything else.

(3)   Toto made Dorothy laugh, and saved her from growing as gray as her other surroundings. Toto was not gray; he was a little black dog, with long silky hair and small black eyes that twinkled merrily on either side of his funny, wee nose. Toto played all day long, and Dorothy played with him, and loved him dearly.

(4)   Today, however, they were not playing. Uncle Henry sat upon the doorstep and looked anxiously at the sky, which was even grayer than usual. Dorothy stood in the door with Toto in her arms, and looked at the sky too. Aunt Em was washing the dishes.

(5)   From the far north they heard a low wail of the wind, and Uncle Henry and Dorothy could see where the long grass bowed in waves before the coming storm. There now came a sharp whistling in the air from the south, and as they turned their eyes that way they saw ripples in the grass coming from that direction also.

(6)   Suddenly Uncle Henry stood up.

(7)   "There's a tornado coming, Em," he called to his wife. "I'll go look after the stock." Then he ran toward the sheds where the cows and horses were kept.

(8)   Aunt Em dropped her work and came to the door. One glance told her of the danger close at hand.

(9)   "Quick, Dorothy!" she screamed. "Run for the cellar!"

When you're reading a story with a lot of dialog, make notes in the text to remind yourself of how the characters feel when they speak. Is the character angry? Frightened? These notes will help you understand the story even better.

Exercises

1. Which inference is supported by details in the first paragraph?

   A. Dorothy and her family have just moved to their house.
   B. There are very few trees where Dorothy and her family live.
   C. It is usually cold and rainy where Dorothy and her family live.
   D. Dorothy and her family live near a small town.

   RL.5.1

4. Which best describes the conflict in this passage?

   A. Dorothy is trying very hard to stay happy and optimistic, even though she lives in an environment that his sad, dull, and gray.
   B. Dorothy and her family are very poor and must work hard to survive as farmers.
   C. Dorothy and her family must get to safety before a dangerous storm arrives.
   D. Dorothy's aunt and uncle don't approve of Dorothy's dog because he is an added expense.

   RL.5.2

2. Who is the narrator or the person telling this story?

   A. Dorothy
   B. A person who is not part of the story, but knows what everyone is thinking.
   C. A person who is not part of the story, and describes the characters' actions and feelings.
   D. A person who is part of the story, but is not Dorothy or her aunt or uncle.

   RI.5.6

5. Reread paragraph 8. What inference can the reader make based on this paragraph?

   A. Aunt Em had seen cyclones before.
   B. Aunt Em was worried that Uncle Henry would not get to safety.
   C. Aunt Em did not know what to do in case of an emergency like this.
   D. Aunt Em did not want Dorothy to bring Toto, the dog, into the shelter.

   RL.5.1

3. Context from this text supports that a tornado is the same thing as a _____.

   A. Cellar
   B. Dog
   C. Wind
   D. Cyclone

   RL.5.4

6. Review paragraph 2. What is the best definition of the word prairie as it is used in this paragraph?

   A. A low, sandy tract of grassland, usually covered in water, which can be filled or reclaimed by draining water from it.
   B. A marsh or swamp
   C. A large flat area of land, covered with coarse grass, and well suited for growing crops.
   D. A type of steam locomotive or engine, which has two front wheels, six supporting wheels, and tows a small two-wheeled container for coal or other fuel.

   RL.5.4

From **Heidi** *by Johanna Spyri*

(http://www.gutenberg.org/ebooks/20781)

(1) On a sunny morning in June two figures were climbing the narrow mountain path. One was a tall strong-looking girl. The other was a child whom she was leading by the hand. The child's little cheeks were so aglow with heat that the crimson color could be seen even through the dark, sunburnt skin. For, in spite of the hot June sun the child was clothed as if to keep off the bitterest frost. She did not look more than five years old, if as much. What her natural figure was like, it would have been hard to say. She had apparently two, if not three dresses, one above the other, and over these a thick red woolen shawl wound round about her. Her little body presented a shapeless appearance, as it slowly and laboriously plodded its way up in the heat.

(2) The two must have left the valley a good hour's walk behind them. They finally came to the hamlet known as Dorfli, which is situated half-way up the mountain. Here the wayfarers met with greetings from all sides. Some called to them from windows, some from open doors. The elder girl was now in her old home. She did not pause in her walk to respond to her friends' welcoming cries and questions. She passed on without stopping for a moment until she reached the last of the scattered houses of the hamlet. Here a voice called to her: "Wait a moment, Dete; if you are going up higher, I will come with you."

(3) The girl stood still, and the child immediately let go her hand and seated herself on the ground.

(4) "Are you tired, Heidi?" asked her companion.

(5) "No, I am hot," answered the child.

(6) "We shall soon get to the top now. You must walk bravely on a little longer, and take good long steps, and in another hour we shall be there," said Dete in an encouraging voice.

(7) They were now joined by a stout, good-natured-looking woman, who walked on ahead with her old acquaintance, the two breaking forth at once into lively conversation about everybody and everything in Dorfli and its surroundings, while the child wandered behind them.

(8) "And where are you off to with the child?" asked the one who had just joined the party. "I suppose it is the child your sister left?"

(9) "Yes," answered Dete. "I am taking her up to Uncle, where she must stay."

(10) "The child stay up there with Alm-Uncle! You must be out of your senses, Dete! How can you think of such a thing! The old man, however, will soon send you and your proposal packing off home again!"

(11) "He cannot very well do that, seeing that he is her grandfather. He must do something for her. I have had the charge of the child till now, and I can tell you, Barbel, I am not going to give up the chance which has just fallen to me of getting a good place, for her sake. It is for the grandfather now to do his duty by her."

Most stories have a conflict or a problem that has to be solved. When annotating a text, identify the problem, and, if possible, the cause of the problem.

Exercises

1. Which statement best explains why the little girl is dressed in several layers?

 A. The weather is very cold and she is wearing all of her clothing in order to stay warm.
 B. She couldn't decide which dress to wear that morning, so she wore several.
 C. She is wearing all her clothing because she is going to a new place to live.
 D. She doesn't want anyone to steal her clothing, so she is wearing all of it.

RL.5.1

2. What conflict is suggested in this passage?

 A. The girl, Heidi, does not want to hike up the mountain.
 B. Heidi's grandfather may not want to take her in.
 C. Barbel wants to keep Heidi with her.
 D. Dete may not be able to walk all the way to "alm-uncle's" house.

RL.5.2

3. How would this story be different if the character Barbel were not introduced?

 A. The reader would not know the purpose of the hike.
 B. The reader would not have a clear understanding of the setting.
 C. The difference between the two main characters would not be described.
 D. The distance the pair had walked would not be included.

RL.5.5

4. Which statement best describes the way Dete treats Heidi?

 A. Dete obviously dislikes Heidi and is impatient with her.
 B. Dete is kind and encouraging to Heidi.
 C. Dete is embarrassed by Heidi and tries to walk ahead of her as though she doesn't know her.
 D. Dete is annoyed that Heidi is following her, and wants her to stop.

RL.5.3

5. Read this excerpt from paragraph 7; what does the phrase "breaking forth," mean in this context?

 "..., the two breaking forth at once into lively conversation about everybody and everything in Dorfli..."

 A. Splitting up
 B. Yelling
 C. Erupting
 D. Interrupting

RL.5.4

6. From whose point of view is this passage told?

 A. An observer in the town of Dorfli
 B. Heidi, the little girl dressed in layers of clothing.
 C. A disinterested observer who is not part of the story.
 D. Barbel, the woman who joins Dete and Heidi on their journey.

RL.5.6

From **Theodore Roosevelt, An Autobiography**

http://www.bartleby.com/55/1.html

The summers we spent in the country, at one place or another. We children, of course, loved the country beyond anything. We disliked the city. We were always wildly eager to get to the country when spring came, and very sad when in the late fall the family moved back to town. In the country we of course had all kinds of pets—cats, dogs, rabbits, a coon, and a sorrel Shetland pony named General Grant. When my younger sister first heard of the real General Grant, by the way, she was much struck by the coincidence that some one should have given him the same name as the pony. (Thirty years later my own children had their pony Grant.) In the country we children ran barefoot much of the time, and the seasons went by in a round of uninterrupted and enthralling pleasures—supervising the haying and harvesting, picking apples, hunting frogs successfully and woodchucks unsuccessfully, gathering hickory-nuts and chestnuts for sale to patient parents, building wigwams in the woods, and sometimes playing Indians in too realistic manner by staining ourselves (and incidentally our clothes) in liberal fashion with poke-cherry juice.

Thanksgiving was an appreciated festival, but it in no way came up to Christmas. Christmas was an occasion of literally delirious joy. In the evening we hung up our stockings—or rather the biggest stockings we could borrow from the grown-ups—and before dawn we trooped in to open them while sitting on father's and mother's bed; and the bigger presents were arranged, those for each child on its own table, in the drawing-room, the doors to which were thrown open after breakfast. I never knew anyone else have what seemed to me such attractive Christmases, and in the next generation I tried to reproduce them exactly for my own children.

I never knew anyone who got greater joy out of living than did my father, or anyone who more whole-heartedly performed every duty; and no one whom I have ever met approached his combination of enjoyment of life and performance of duty. He and my mother were given to a hospitality that at that time was associated more commonly with southern than northern households; and, especially in their later years when they had moved up town, in the neighborhood of Central Park, they kept a charming, open house.

My father worked hard at his business, for he died when he was forty-six, too early to have retired. He was interested in every social reform movement, and he did an immense amount of practical charitable work himself. He was a big, powerful man, with a leonine face, and his heart filled with gentleness for those who needed help or protection, and with the possibility of much wrath against a bully or an oppressor.

  *An autobiography is written by a person about his or her own life. In an autobiography, the narrator is the subject of the text. Autobiographies are informational texts. Look for instances when the narrator makes a reference to a time in his past to explain or add detail to an event or situation in his present.*

Exercises

1. What did the narrator's sister think when she learned that there was a military leader named "General Grant?"

RI.5.2

2. What details does the narrator include to support his claim that his father got "great joy out of living?"

RI.5.8

Exercises

3. How did the narrator's childhood influence his life as an adult?

A. He so admired his father that he decided to go into the same business.
B. He raised his family in the country, which he always liked more than the city.
C. He has worked hard to make Christmas for his family as wonderful as Christmas when he was a child.
D. He believes it is very important to have friends and to invite people to his home, showing the same hospitality as his parents.

RI.5.3

5. What does the word "wholeheartedly" mean in the sentence below:

"...or anyone who more wholeheartedly performed every duty...:

A. Enthusiastically
B. Affectionately
C. Insincerely
D. Deceitfully

RI.5.4

4. What media would best support the details the author includes in this text?

A. A film set during the same time period.
B. A recording of the author reading the text.
C. A document that lists the members of the narrator's family, their names, and their dates of birth.
D. Photos of the narrator and his family when he was a child.

RI.5.7

6. Which quote from the text supports the inference that the narrator's father was very generous?

A. I never knew anyone who got greater joy out of living than did my father, or anyone who more whole-heartedly performed every duty;
B. He was interested in every social reform movement...
C. ...he did an immense amount of practical charitable work himself...
D. He and my mother were given to a hospitality that at that time was associated more commonly with southern than northern households;

RL.5.1

WEEK 4

VIDEO EXPLANATIONS

ARGOPREP.COM

From **U.S. History: The Westward Spirit**

Download for free at http://cnx.org/contents/a7ba2fb8-8925-4987-b182-5f4429d48daa@3.32.

The Homestead Act allowed any head of household, or individual over the age of twenty-one—including unmarried women—to receive a parcel of 160 acres for only a nominal filing fee. All that recipients were required to do in exchange was to "improve the land" within a period of five years of taking possession. The standards for improvement were minimal: Owners could clear a few acres, build small houses or barns, or maintain livestock. Under this act, the government transferred over 270 million acres of public domain land to private citizens.

The Pacific Railway Act was pivotal in helping settlers move west more quickly, as well as move their farm products, and later cattle and mining deposits, back east. The first of many railway initiatives, this act commissioned the Union Pacific Railroad to build new track west from Omaha, Nebraska, while the Central Pacific Railroad moved east from Sacramento, California. The law provided each company with ownership of all public lands within two hundred feet on either side of the track laid, as well as additional land grants and payment through load bonds, prorated on the difficulty of the terrain it crossed. Because of these provisions, both companies made a significant profit, whether they were crossing hundreds of miles of open plains, or working their way through the Sierra Nevada Mountains of California. As a result, the nation's first transcontinental railroad was completed when the two companies connected their tracks at Promontory Point, Utah, in the spring of 1869. Other tracks, including lines radiating from this original one, subsequently created a network that linked all corners of the nation.

In addition to legislation designed to facilitate western settlement, the U.S. government assumed an active role on the ground, building numerous forts throughout the West to protect and assist settlers during their migration. Forts such as Fort Laramie in Wyoming (built in 1834) and Fort Apache in Arizona (1870) served as protection from nearby Indians as well as maintained peace between potential warring tribes. Others located throughout Colorado and Wyoming became important trading posts for miners and fur trappers. Those built in Kansas, Nebraska, and the Dakotas served primarily to provide relief for farmers during times of drought or related hardships. Forts constructed along the California coastline provided protection in the wake of the Mexican-American War as well as during the American Civil War. These locations subsequently serviced the U.S. Navy and provided important support for growing Pacific trade routes. Whether as army posts constructed for the protection of settlers and to maintain peace among Indian tribes, or as trading posts to further facilitate the development of the region, such forts proved to be important contributions to westward migration.

To better understand a text with many specific terms, dates, and names, highlight key information and annotate, or add your own notes in the margin of the page.

Exercises

1. Which quote from the text supports the inference that the Homestead Act was successful in its goal to encourage people to move to the west?

A. The Homestead Act allowed any head of household, or individual over the age of twenty-one—including unmarried women—to receive a parcel of 160 acres for only a nominal filing fee.
B. All that recipients were required to do in exchange was to "improve the land" within a period of five years of taking possession.
C. The standards for improvement were minimal: Owners could clear a few acres, build small houses or barns, or maintain livestock.
D. Under this act, the government transferred over 270 million acres of public domain land to private citizens.

RI.5.1

2. Which word is a synonym for "pivotal" as it is used in the sentence below:

"The Pacific Railway Act was pivotal in helping settlers move west more quickly, as well as move their farm products, and later cattle and mining deposits, back east."

A. Minor
B. Expensive
C. Early
D. Important

RI.5.4

3. Which statement best describes what the government meant by the phrase "improve the land" when it made this a condition for receiving property in the west?

A. To make some effort to settle on the land with a home or farm
B. To raise livestock such as cattle
C. To build a permanent home
D. To develop a community of several settlers that would support one another.

RI.5.4

4. What is not an example of how the United States government protected settlers who migrated west?

A. Building the railroads
B. Building forts
C. Offering settlers protection from native tribes
D. Helping settlers during times when water or food were scarce

RI.5.2

5. The main way the United States government encouraged people and businesses to move to the western territories was by...

A. Building forts to protect them from warring indigenous people
B. Providing land to women as well as men
C. Giving away land for free or very low costs
D. Intervening during a war with Mexico to make sure settlers and railroad owners were safe

RI.5.2

6. What area did the first transcontinental railroad cover?

A. From the east coast to the west coast
B. From New York to California
C. From New York to Nebraska
D. From Nebraska to California

RI.5.2

From **U.S. History: The Depths of the Great Depression**

Download for free at http://cnx.org/contents/a7ba2fb8-8925-4987-b182-5f4429d48daa@3.32.

(1) By the end of 1932, the Great Depression had affected some sixty million people, most of whom wealthier Americans perceived as the "deserving poor." Yet, at the time, federal efforts to help those in need were extremely limited, and national charities had neither the capacity nor the will to elicit the large-scale response required to address the problem. The American Red Cross did exist, but Chairman John Barton Payne contended that unemployment was not an "Act of God" but rather an "Act of Man," and therefore refused to get involved in widespread direct relief efforts. Clubs like the Elks tried to provide food, as did small groups of individually organized college students. Religious organizations remained on the front lines, offering food and shelter. In larger cities, breadlines and soup lines became a common sight. At one count in 1932, there were as many as eighty-two breadlines in New York City.

(2) Despite these efforts, however, people were destitute and ultimately starving. Families would first run through any savings, if they were lucky enough to have any. Then, the few who had insurance would cash out their policies. Cash surrender payments of individual insurance policies tripled in the first three years of the Great Depression, with insurance companies issuing total payments in excess of $1.2 billion in 1932 alone. When those funds were depleted, people would borrow from family and friends, and when they could get no more, they would simply stop paying rent or mortgage payments. When evicted, they would move in with relatives, whose own situation was likely only a step or two behind. The added burden of additional people would speed along that family's demise, and the cycle would continue. This situation spiraled downward, and did so quickly. Even as late as 1939, over 60 percent of rural households, and 82 percent of farm families, were classified as "impoverished." In larger urban areas, unemployment levels exceeded the national average, with over half a million unemployed workers in Chicago, and nearly a million in New York City. Breadlines and soup kitchens were packed, serving as many as eighty-five thousand meals daily in New York City alone. Over fifty thousand New York citizens were homeless by the end of 1932.

(3) Children, in particular, felt the brunt of poverty. Many in coastal cities would roam the docks in search of spoiled vegetables to bring home. Elsewhere, children begged at the doors of more well-off neighbors, hoping for stale bread, table scraps, or raw potato peelings. Said one childhood survivor of the Great Depression, "You get used to hunger. After the first few days it doesn't even hurt; you just get weak." In 1931 alone, there were at least twenty documented cases of starvation; in 1934, that number grew to 110. In rural areas where such documentation was lacking, the number was likely far higher. And while the middle class did not suffer from starvation, they experienced hunger as well.

Use a highlighter to mark any unfamiliar words. As you read look for context clues. Context clues can be in sentences before or after the word.

Exercises

1. Which statement from the text best supports the conclusion that it is not really known how seriously the Great Depression affected those living in rural areas?

   A. Even as late as 1939, over 60 percent of rural households, and 82 percent of farm families, were classified as "impoverished."
   B. Elsewhere, children begged at the doors of more well-off neighbors, hoping for stale bread, table scraps, or raw potato peelings.
   C. In rural areas where such documentation was lacking, the number was likely far higher.
   D. This situation spiraled downward, and did so quickly.

   RL5.1

2. Paragraph 1 of this passage is mainly about...

   A. The number of people affected by the Great Depression
   B. The causes of the Great Depression
   C. How college students helped people during the Great Depression
   D. How charities responded to the Great Depression

   RI.5.2

3. According to the passage, which of the following statements is true?

   A. People in cities were more likely than those on farms to experience hunger and starvation.
   B. People in rural areas were more likely than those in cities to become homeless.
   C. People in cities recovered from the Great Depression more quickly than those in rural areas.
   D. People in rural areas were more likely to endure starvation than those in the cities.

   RI.5.3

4. According to this passage, why didn't the Red Cross engage in relief efforts during the Great Depression?

   A. The president of the Red Cross was not convinced that all poor people were "deserving" of their help.
   B. The president of the Red Cross did not consider the Great Depression a natural disaster, so it was not something the Red Cross was intended to help with.
   C. Religious organizations were already providing relief, so there was no need for the Red Cross.
   D. The Red Cross was centered in the cities, and most of the help was needed in rural, farming areas.

   RI.5.4

5. According to paragraph 2, what was an effect of people moving in with relatives after they'd run out of money?

   A. The breadlines in the cities grew longer and longer.
   B. People were impoverished for longer periods of time.
   C. The relatives would run out of money more quickly.
   D. People who moved in with relatives were evicted from their own homes.

   RI.5.5

6. The main idea of paragraph 3 is...

   A. Children, in particular, suffered tremendously during the Great Depression.
   B. Hunger is something people can grow accustomed to, and is seldom fatal.
   C. There is no way to know how many people died of starvation during the Great Depression.
   D. Children who lived in coastal cities were able to find food more easily than those who lived in the country.

   RI.5.2

Find detailed video explanations to each problem on:
ArgoPrep.com

From **The Story of Doctor Dolittle** *by Hugh Lofting*

(http://www.gutenberg.org/ebooks/501)

(1) ONCE upon a time, there was a doctor; and his name was Dolittle--John Dolittle, M.D. "M.D." means that he was a proper doctor and knew a whole lot.

(2) He lived in a little town called, Puddleby-on-the-Marsh. All the folks, young and old, knew him well by sight. And whenever he walked down the street in his high hat everyone would say, "There goes the Doctor!--He's a clever man." And the dogs and the children would all run up and follow behind him; and even the crows that lived in the church-tower would caw and nod their heads

(3) The house he lived in, on the edge of the town, was quite small; but his garden was very large and had a wide lawn and stone seats and weeping-willows hanging over. His sister, Sarah Dolittle, was housekeeper for him; but the Doctor looked after the garden himself.

(4) He was very fond of animals and kept many kinds of pets. Besides the gold-fish in the pond at the bottom of his garden, he had rabbits in the pantry, white mice in his piano, a squirrel in the linen closet and a hedgehog in the cellar. He had a cow with a calf too, and an old lame horse-twenty-five years of age--and chickens, and pigeons, and two lambs, and many other animals. But his favorite pets were Dab-Dab the duck, Jip the dog, Gub-Gub the baby pig, Polynesia the parrot, and the owl Too-Too.

(5) His sister used to grumble about all these animals and said they made the house untidy. And one day when an old lady with rheumatism came to see the Doctor, she sat on the hedgehog who was sleeping on the sofa and never came to see him any more, but drove every Saturday all the way to Oxenthorpe, another town ten miles off, to see a different doctor.

(6) Then his sister, Sarah Dolittle, came to him and said, "John, how can you expect sick people to come and see you when you keep all these animals in the house? It's a fine doctor would have his parlor full of hedgehogs and mice! That's the fourth personage these animals have driven away. If you go on like this, none of the best people will have you for a doctor."

(7) "But I like the animals better than the 'best people'," said the Doctor.

(8) "You are ridiculous," said his sister, and walked out of the room.

(9) So, as time went on, the Doctor got more and more animals; and the people who came to see him got less and less. Till at last he had no one left—but one man, who wasn't very rich and only got sick once a year--at Christmas-time, when he used to give the Doctor sixpence for a bottle of medicine.

A character's tone is his or her attitude. You can determine a character's tone by looking closely at her words and actions, and at clues the narrator gives you. For example, if a character storms out of a room after saying something, you can determine the character is angry or frustrated.

Exercises

1. What can the reader infer about how Dr. Dolittle feels about his reputation with the "best people?"

_____

_____

_____

_____

_____

_____

_____

_____

_____

_____

RL.5.1

2. Using evidence from the text, explain why Sarah Dolittle is not happy about her brother's interest in animals.

_____

_____

_____

_____

_____

_____

_____

_____

_____

RL.5.1

Exercises

3. The author develops the narrator's point of view by...

   A. Using a first-person narrative that includes the narrator's thoughts and feelings.
   B. Using a third-person narrator who focuses on how others react to the protagonist.
   C. Explaining details that are known to the narrator but not to the reader or other characters.
   D. Using a third person point of view that includes the thoughts of the protagonist.

   RL.5.6

4. Which sentence would be best to include in a short summary of this passage?

   A. One of Dr. Dolittle's favorite pets was a duck.
   B. The letters "M.D." at the end of Dolittle's name meant he "knew a whole lot."
   C. Dr. Dolittle lost three patients before the old lady with rheumatism left him for a doctor in Oxenthorpe.
   D. Dolittle realized that children and animals were not concerned with money.

   RL.5.2

5. Read the sentence below from paragraph 2 and drag and drop the words that could replace the word clever in this sentence with the same meaning.

   There goes the doctor – He's a ___ man.

   A. Smart
   B. Witty
   C. Sly
   D. Sensible

   RL.5.4

6. How is paragraph 9 in the passage related to paragraph 6?

   A. Paragraph 9 shows that Sarah was wrong about how patients would react to the doctor's interest in animals.
   B. Paragraph 9 shows the results of the doctor following his sister's advice.
   C. Paragraph 9 shows that Sarah was right when she warned the doctor about his animals.
   D. Paragraph 9 shows that the doctor cares about his sister and her opinions.

   RL.5.5

WEEK 5

VIDEO
EXPLANATIONS

ARGOPREP.COM

How the Whale Got His Throat - Adapted from a story *by Rudyard Kipling*

(http://www.gutenberg.org/files/2781/2781-h/2781-h.htm)

(1)   IN the sea, once upon a time, there was a Whale, and he ate fishes. All the fishes he could find in all the sea he ate! Until, at last there was only one small fish left in all the sea, and he was a small 'Stute Fish. The 'Stute fish swam behind the Whale's right ear, so as to be out of harm's way. Then the Whale stood up on his tail and said, "I'm hungry." And the small 'Stute Fish said in a small 'stute voice,

(2)   "Noble and generous whale, have you ever tasted Man?"

(3)   "No," said the Whale. "What is it like?"

(4)   "Nice," said the small 'Stute Fish. "Nice but nubbly."

(5)   "Then fetch me some," said the Whale, and he slapped the water with his tail.

(6)   "One at a time is enough," said the 'Stute Fish. "If you swim to latitude Fifty North, longitude Forty West you will find a man. He is sitting on a raft, in the middle of the sea, with nothing on but a pair of blue canvas breeches and a pair of suspenders. He's a shipwrecked sailor. All he has with him is a small jackknife"

(7)   So the Whale swam and swam to latitude Fifty North, longitude Forty West, as fast as he could swim. There he found the sailor, sitting on a raft, dragging his toes in the water.

(8)   The Whale opened his mouth back and back and back till it nearly touched his tail, and he swallowed the sailor, and the raft he was sitting on. He swallowed them all down and then he smacked his lips and turned round three times on his tail.

(8)   But as soon as the sailor, who was a resourceful and determined man, found himself inside the Whale's stomach he stumped and he jumped and he thumped and he bumped. He danced all over. The Whale felt most unhappy indeed.

(9)   The whale said to the 'Stute Fish, "This man is very nubbly. He is making me hiccough. What shall I do?"

(10)   "Tell him to come out," said the 'Stute Fish.

(11)   So the Whale called down his own throat to the sailor, "Come out and behave yourself. I've got the hiccoughs."

(12)   "Nope!" said the Mariner. "Not until you take me to land. Take me to the white cliffs on the seashore. Then I'll come out."

Sometimes an author gives you a hint about what might happen later in the story. This is called foreshadowing. For example, an author might tell you what kind of person a character is. Pay attention to details about a character, and as the story goes on, try to predict how or why those characteristics will be important.

(13) "You had better take him home," said the 'Stute Fish to the Whale. "I ought to have warned you that he is very stubborn and determined."

(14) So the Whale swam and swam and swam, with both flippers and his tail, as hard as he could even with hiccoughs. At last he saw white cliffs of the sea shore and he stopped.

(15) While the Whale had been swimming, the sailor, who was resourceful, had taken his jack-knife and cut up the raft into a little square grating all running criss-cross. He dragged that grating good and tight into the Whale's throat, and there it stuck! Then the sailor said, "Never again will you swallow a sailor and his raft all at once. Now you'll have to eat tiny food that will fit through the grating!"

(16) The sailor walked out of the whale's mouth went home to his mother. But from that day on, the grating in whale's throat, which he could neither cough up nor swallow down, prevented him eating anything except very, very small fish. That is the reason why whales nowadays never eat men or boys or little girls.

(17) The small 'Stute Fish went and hid himself in the mud under the Door-sills of the Equator. He was a very small fish with very bad ideas.

Exercises

1. What inference can the reader make from paragraph 17?

   A. Whales don't eat 'Stute Fish.
   B. The 'Stute Fish was afraid of the whale.
   C. The 'Stute Fish was afraid of the man.
   D. The 'Stute Fish was sorry he tricked whale.

RL.5.1

2. Which best describes the narrator in this story?

   A. A first person narrator describing events as he saw them.
   B. A third person narrator who is relating a story he was not a part of.
   C. A first person narrator who is one of the characters in the story.
   D. A third person narrator who is relating a story told to him by one of the characters.

RL.5.6

3. How are the 'Stute fish and the man similar?

   A. Both are victims of the whale.
   B. Both are afraid of the whale.
   C. Both try to reason with the whale.
   D. Both outsmart the whale.

RL.5.3

4. What is the main conflict in this story?

   A. A whale is trying to find something to eat.
   B. A small fish is trying to outsmart a whale so he can survive.
   C. A whale is trying to outsmart a man.
   D. A man is trying to save his own life

RL.5.2

5. What does the word "nubbly" mean as it is used in this passage?

   A. Rough and uncomfortable
   B. Stubborn and determined
   C. Clever and tricky
   D. Spoiled and not good to eat

RL.5.4

Find detailed video explanations to each problem on:
ArgoPrep.com

Adapted from **Ruth of Boston** *by James Otis*

(http://www.gutenberg.org/files/44100/44100-h/44100-h.htm)

A PROPER BEGINNING

(1) TRULY it seems a great undertaking to journey from London into the land of America, yet I have done so. There are very few twelve-year-old girls likely to make such a voyage. It seems to me I should write about the things I saw and did. It might be interesting to myself in the future, when I shall have grown to be an old lady or to anyone who may come upon this diary.

(2) Of course I must first set down who I am, in case strangers should someday chance to find this book, and, growing interested in it for who can say that I may not be able to tell a story which shall be entertaining, because of there being in it much which the people of England have never seen—give me credit for having written a diary without a proper beginning.

(3) You must know, then, that my name is Ruth. In the year of our Lord, 1630, when, as I have said, I was but twelve years of age, my father joined that company led by Master John Winthrop, whose intent it was to go into America to spread the gospel, and there also build up a town wherein should live only those who were one with them in the worship of God.

(4) This company was made up of four classes of people. First there were those who paid a sum of money for their passage to America, and, because of having done so, were to be given a certain number of acres of land in the New World.

(5) In the second class were those who, not having enough money to pay the full price for their passage, agreed to perform a sufficient amount of work, after arriving in America, to make up for the same.

(6) In the third class were those called indentured servants, which is much the same as if I said apprentices. The fourth and last class had in it those people who were to work for wages, at whatsoever trade or calling they were best fitted.

(7) It needs not that I should say more by way of a beginning, for surely all the people in England, if they do not know it now, will soon come to understand why we, together with those who have gone before us, and the companies that are to come after, have journeyed into America.

(8) It was decided that my parents, and, of course, myself, should sail in the same ship with Master Winthrop, and the name of that vessel was the Arabella, she having been so called in honor of Lady Arabella Johnson, who journeyed with us.

  *Even in works of fiction there can be a purpose to a text. Some texts are framed as journals, diaries, or other types of documents. Identify the purpose and format of a text as soon as you begin reading it. It will help you understand the main points.*

(9) My mother was sadly grieved because of Mistress Winthrop's deciding not to go on the voyage with her husband, but to join him in the New World later, and this decision was a disappointment to very many of the company. I am in doubt as to whether the Lady Arabella would have gone with us on this ship, had she not believed Mistress Winthrop also was to go.

(10) It was on the twenty-second day of March, in that year which I have previously set down, that, having already journeyed from London to Southampton, we went aboard the Arabella, counting that the voyage would be begun without delay, and yet, because of unfriendly winds and cruel storms, our ship, with three others of the company, lay at anchor until the eighth day of April.

(11) Then it was, after the captain of the ship had shot off three guns as a farewell, that we sailed out on the broad ocean, where we were tossed by the waves and buffeted by the winds for nine long, dreary weeks."

Exercises

1. Why is the narrator writing this passage?

    A. To be sure she has a good record of her adventure.
    B. To record her experience for herself and others in the future.
    C. To help her mother keep track of events.
    D. To tell her friends in London about her trip.

    RL.5.1

2. What problem delayed the start of the voyage?

    A. Mrs. Winthrop decided not to travel on the ship.
    B. Lady Arabella refused to travel unless the ship was named for her.
    C. The trip from London to Southampton was longer than expected.
    D. The sea was rough and choppy and not suited for leaving.

    RL.5.2

3. Which of the classes described does Ruth's family most likely belong to?

    A. First
    B. Second
    C. Third
    D. Fourth

    RL.5.1

4. What does the word "intent" mean as it is used in paragraph 3?

    A. Regret
    B. Goal
    C. Wish
    D. Dream

    RL.5.4

5. This text can best be described as a...

    A. Friendly letter
    B. Official document
    C. Diary entry
    D. Notes about a dream

    RL.5.6

6. Paragraphs 5 and 6 provide what information about the characters in the story?

    A. All of them were religious people following Master Winthrop
    B. Most would be land owners in the new world.
    C. They all came from similar backgrounds.
    D. Some would have to work for others as soon as they got to the new world.

    RL.5.3

From **Introduction to Sociology 2e**

Download for free at http://cnx.org/contents/afe4332a-c97f-4fc4-be27-4e4d384a32d8@7.23.

What is Technology?

(1) While most people probably picture computers and cell phones when the subject of technology comes up, technology is not merely a product of the modern era. For example, fire and stone tools were important forms that technology developed during the Stone Age. Just as the availability of digital technology shapes how we live today, the creation of stone tools changed how premodern humans lived and how well they ate. From the first calculator, invented in 2400 B.C.E. Babylon in the form of an abacus, to the predecessor of the modern computer, created in 1882 by Charles Babbage, all of our technological innovations are advancements on previous iterations. And indeed, all aspects of our lives today are influenced by technology. In agriculture, the introduction of machines that can till, thresh, plant, and harvest greatly reduced the need for manual labor, which in turn meant there were fewer rural jobs. This led to the urbanization of society, as well as lowered birthrates because there was less need for large families to work the farms. In the criminal justice system, the ability to ascertain innocence through DNA testing has saved the lives of people on death row. The examples are endless: technology plays a role in absolutely every aspect of our lives.

Use of Technology and Social Media

(2) Do you own an e-reader or tablet? What about your parents or your friends? How often do you check social media or your cell phone? Despite the many advantages of these technologies, there may be a downside. When it comes to cell phones, 67 percent of users check their phones for messages or calls even when the phone wasn't ringing. In addition, "44% of cell owners have slept with their phone next to their bed because they wanted to make sure they didn't miss any calls, text messages, or other updates during the night and 29% of cell owners describe their cell phone as 'something they can't imagine living without'" (Smith 2012).

(3) While people report that cell phones make it easier to stay in touch, simplify planning and scheduling their daily activities, and increase their productivity, that's not the only impact of increased cell phone ownership in the United States. Smith also reports that "roughly one in five cell owners say that their phone has made it at least somewhat harder to forget about work at home or on the weekends; to give people their undivided attention; or to focus on a single task without being distracted" (Smith 2012).

(4) A new survey from the Pew Research Center reported that 73 percent of adults engage in some sort of social networking online. Facebook was the most popular platform, and both Facebook users and Instagram users check their sites on a daily basis. Over a third of users check their sites more than once a day (Duggan and Smith 2013).

(5) With so many people using social media both in the United States and abroad, it is no surprise that social media is a powerful force for social change. For example, McKenna Pope, a thirteen-year-old

Information in parentheses after a statistic or fact is a citation. This information refers to another text the author used for research while writing the article. When you see a citation after information, you know it is most likely accurate and credible.

girl, used the Internet to successfully petition Hasbro to fight gender stereotypes by creating a gender-neutral Easy-Bake Oven instead of using only the traditional pink color (Kumar 2014). Meanwhile in Latvia, two twenty-three-year-olds used a U.S. State Department grant to create an e-petition platform so citizens could submit ideas directly to the Latvian government. If at least 20 percent of the Latvian population (roughly 407,200 people) supports a petition, the government will look at it (Kumar 2014).

Exercises

1. What does the author mean in the first paragraph when he writes, "Technology is not just a product of the modern era?"

RI.5.1

2. What is the main idea of the last paragraph of this passage?

RL.5.2

Exercises

3. Which quote provides evidence to support the author's point that there is a "downside" to modern technology?

    A. The examples are endless: technology plays a role in absolutely every aspect of our lives.
    B. With so many people using social media both in the United States and abroad, it is no surprise that social media is a powerful force for social change.
    C. Over a third of users check their sites more than once a day.
    D. Roughly one in five cell owners say that their phone has made it at least somewhat harder to forget about work at home or on the weekends...

    RI.5.1

4. What is the most likely reason the author included the following information: "When it comes to cell phones, 67 percent of users check their phones for messages or calls even when the phone wasn't ringing."

    A. To show that the majority of people own cell phones.
    B. To show that people think about their phones even when they aren't using them.
    C. To show that is difficult to know when one has a message on his or her phone.
    D. To show how phone usage has changed over the years.

    RI.5.8

5. What does the phrase "engage in" mean in the following sentence, "A new survey from the Pew Research Center reported that 73 percent of adults engage in some sort of social networking online."

    A. Participate in
    B. Know of
    C. Share personal information on
    D. Have too much dependence on

    RI.5.4

6. What is the main idea of paragraph 2?

    A. Many people own phones, tablets, and e-readers.
    B. Some people use their phones instead of talking to people.
    C. Many phone users are afraid they'll miss something if they don't check their phones frequently.
    D. Some people who own phones also have other forms of technology, such as tablets and e-readers.

    RI.5.2

WEEK 6

VIDEO EXPLANATIONS

ARGOPREP.COM

From **The Adventures of Peter Pan** by J.M. Barrie

http://literature.org/authors/barrie-james-matthew/the-adventures-of-peter-pan/chapter-01.html

(1)　Mrs. Darling loved to have everything just so, and Mr. Darling had a passion for being exactly like his neighbors; so, of course, they had a nanny. As they were poor, owing to the amount of milk the children drank, this nanny was a prim Newfoundland dog, called Nana, who had belonged to no one until the Darlings engaged her. She had always thought children important, however, and the Darlings had become acquainted with her in Kensington Gardens, where she spent most of her spare time peeping into strollers, and was much hated by careless nursemaids, whom she followed to their homes and complained of to their mistresses. She proved to be quite a treasure of a nanny. How thorough she was at bath-time, and up at any moment of the night if one of her charges made the slightest cry. Of course, her kennel was in the nursery. She had a genius for knowing when a cough is a thing to have no patience with and when it needs stocking around your throat. She believed to her last day in old-fashioned remedies like rhubarb leaf, and made sounds of contempt over all this new-fangled talk about germs, and so on. It was a lesson in propriety to see her escorting the children to school, walking sedately by their side when they were well behaved, and butting them back into line if they strayed. On John's footer [in England, soccer was called football, "footer" for short] days she never once forgot his sweater, and she usually carried an umbrella in her mouth in case of rain. There is a room in the basement of Miss Fulsom's school where the nannies wait. They sat on forms, while Nana lay on the floor, but that was the only difference. They affected to ignore her as of an inferior social status to themselves, and she despised their light talk. She resented visits to the nursery from Mrs. Darling's friends, but if they did come she first whipped off Michael's pinafore and put him into the one with blue braiding, and smoothed out Wendy and made a dash at John's hair.

(2)　No nursery could possibly have been conducted more correctly, and Mr. Darling knew it, yet he sometimes wondered uneasily whether the neighbors talked.

(3)　He had his position in the city to consider.

(4)　Nana also troubled him in another way. He had sometimes a feeling that she did not admire him. "I know she admires you tremendously, George," Mrs. Darling would assure him, and then she would sign to the children to be especially nice to father. Lovely dances followed, in which the only other servant, Liza, was sometimes allowed to join. So young she looked in her long skirt and maid's cap, though she had sworn, when engaged, that she would never see ten again. The gaiety of those romps! And gayest of all was Mrs. Darling, who would pirouette so wildly that all you could see of her was the kiss, and then if you had dashed at her you might have got it. There never was a simpler happier family until the coming of Peter Pan.

TIP of the DAY

Expect the unexpected – don't forget that literature can be fantastic and introduce ideas that seem completely ridiculous and silly. When that happens, try to "suspend disbelief." That's an old expression that means you try to forget that what you're reading is completely unbelievable, so that you can understand the story.

Exercises

1. What can the reader tell about the Darling family from reading paragraph 4?

   A. Mr. and Mrs. Darling were very young.
   B. They found joy in one another.
   C. They knew their happiness would not last.
   D. They were wealthy and had many servants.

RL.5.3

2. A nanny is a person hired by a family to look after the children of the family. What is unique about the Darling's nanny, Nana?

   A. She is a relative.
   B. She is better than most other nannies.
   C. She is a dog.
   D. She is not particularly fond of children.

RL.5.4

3. What does the last sentence of the passage suggest about the Darling family?

   A. Their lives will be different when Peter Pan arrives.
   B. Peter Pan will make them even happier.
   C. They will stop dancing when Peter Pan arrives.
   D. Peter Pan is one of their children, and he does not get along with others.

RL.5.3

4. How does Mr. Darling feel about Nana?

   A. He wonders if she is doing a good job.
   B. He worries what the neighbors think of her.
   C. He is concerned that she doesn't respect the children.
   D. He does not think she is old enough for the job she has.

RL.5.2

5. What is the difference between Nana and other nannies at the children's school?

   A. Nana lay on the floor while waiting for the children, unlike the other nannies.
   B. Nana always carried an umbrella for her children, unlike the other nannies.
   C. The other nannies were content to wait in the basement for the children, unlike Nana.
   D. The other nannies had fewer children to look after than did Nana.

RL.5.3

6. What does the phrase "new fangled" mean in this sentence from paragraph 1: "this new-fangled talk about germs, and so on..."

   A. Unproven
   B. Silly
   C. Foreign
   D. Modern

RL.5.4

From **"The Adventures of Grandfather Frog"** *By Thorton W. Burgess*

(https://www.gutenberg.org/files/14375/14375-h/14375-h.htm)

Billy Mink Finds Little Joe Otter

(1) Billy Mink ran around the edge of the Smiling Pool and turned down by the Laughing Brook. His eyes twinkled with mischief, and he hurried as only Billy can. As he passed Jerry Muskrat's house, Jerry saw him.

(2) "Hi, Billy Mink! Where are you going in such a hurry this fine morning?" he called.

(3) "To find Little Joe Otter. Have you seen anything of him?" replied Billy.

(4) "No," said Jerry. "He's probably down to the Big River fishing. I heard him say last night that he was going."

(5) "Thanks," said Billy Mink, and without waiting to say more he was off like a little brown flash.

(6) Jerry watched him out of sight. "Hump!" exclaimed Jerry. "Billy Mink is in a terrible hurry this morning. Now I wonder what he is so anxious to find Little Joe Otter for. When they get their heads together, it is usually for some mischief."

(7) Jerry climbed to the top of his house and looked over the Smiling Pool in the direction from which Billy Mink had just come. Almost at once he saw Grandfather Frog fast asleep on his big green lily-pad. The legs of a foolish green fly were sticking out of one corner of his big mouth. Jerry couldn't help laughing, for Grandfather Frog certainly did look funny.

(8) "He's had a good breakfast this morning, and his full stomach has made him sleepy," thought Jerry. "But he's getting careless in his old age. He certainly is getting careless. The idea of going to sleep right out in plain sight like that!"

(9) Suddenly a new thought popped into his head. "Billy Mink saw him, and that is why he is so anxious to find Little Joe Otter. He is planning to play some trick on Grandfather Frog as sure as pollywogs have tails!" exclaimed Jerry. Then his eyes began to twinkle as he added: "I think I'll have some fun myself."

(10) Without another word Jerry slipped down into the water and swam over to the big green lily-pad of Grandfather Frog. Then he hit the water a smart blow with his tail. Grandfather Frog's big goggly eyes flew open, and he was just about to make a frightened plunge into the Smiling Pool when he saw Jerry.

(11) "Have a nice nap?" inquired Jerry, with a broad grin.

(12) "I wasn't asleep!" protested Grandfather Frog indignantly. "I was just thinking."

(13) "Don't you think it a rather dangerous plan to think so long with your eyes closed?" asked Jerry.

(14) "Well, maybe I did just doze off," admitted Grandfather Frog sheepishly.

(15) "Maybe you did," replied Jerry. "Now listen." Then Jerry whispered in Grandfather Frog's ear, and both chuckled as if they were enjoying some joke, for they are great friends, you know. Afterward Jerry swam back to his house, and Grandfather Frog closed his eyes so as to look just as he did when he was asleep.

An inference is a conclusion you come to based on information in the text and what you already know about the world around you. If you are making an inference, start by looking at the text and thinking about what is going on "between the lines," or what you would understand if you were a part of the story.

(16)   Meanwhile Billy Mink had hurried down the Laughing Brook. Half-way to the Big River he met Little Joe Otter bringing home a big fish, for you know Little Joe is a great fisherman. Billy Mink hastened to tell him how Grandfather Frog had fallen fast asleep on his big green lily-pad.

(17)   "It's a splendid chance to have some fun with Grandfather Frog and give him a great scare," concluded Billy.

(18)   Little Joe Otter put his fish down and grinned. He likes to play pranks almost as well as he likes to go fishing.

(19)   "What can we do?" said he.

(20)   "I've thought of a plan," replied Billy. "Do you happen to know where we can find Longlegs the Blue Heron?"

(21)   "Yes," said Little Joe. "I saw him fishing not five minutes ago."

(22)   Then Billy told Little Joe his plan, and laughing and giggling, the two little scamps hurried off to find Longlegs the Blue Heron.

Exercises

1. What makes Jerry suspicious of Billy Mink?

  A. Billy keeps looking at Grandfather
  B. Billy seems like he's in a great hurry.
  C. Billy is awake much earlier than usual.
  D. Billy refused to tell him why he was looking for Little Joe Otter.

  RL.5.3

2. What will likely happen when Billy and Joe try to play a trick on Grandfather?

  A. He will be scared and angry with them.
  B. Jerry will be upset with them.
  C. They will find out it wasn't really funny to frighten the old toad.
  D. They will be outsmarted by Grandfather.

  RL.5.1

3. What is the purpose of paragraph 15 in the text?

  A. It introduces Grandfather.
  B. It shows that Jerry tried to warn Grandfather but he didn't listen, so he'll likely be tricked.
  C. It gives the reader information about Billy's plan so they know what will happen next.
  D. It gives the reader information so they know that Billy's plan may fail.

  RL.5.5

4. Which quote best supports the inference that Jerry is concerned about Grandfather?

  A. Then Jerry whispered in Grandfather Frog's ear, and both chuckled as if they were enjoying some joke...
  B. He certainly is getting careless. The idea of going to sleep right out in plain sight like that!
  C. Without another word Jerry slipped down into the water and swam over to the big green lily-pad of Grandfather Frog.
  D. Afterward Jerry swam back to his house, and Grandfather Frog closed his eyes so as to look just as he did when he was asleep.

  RL.5.1

5. How does the narrator's point of view influence how events in the story are described?

  A. The narrator gives the reader an opportunity to know more than the characters in the story.
  B. The narrator gives the reader an opportunity to understand one character's thoughts and feelings.
  C. The narrator encourages the reader to dislike one or more of the characters.
  D. The narrator knows the thoughts and feelings of two of the characters and shares them with the reader.

  RL.5.6

From **Little Lord Fauntleroy** *By Frances Hodgson Burnett*

(https://www.gutenberg.org/files/479/479-h/479-h.htm)

(1) Cedric himself knew nothing whatever about it. It had never been even mentioned to him. He knew that his papa had been an Englishman, because his mamma had told him so; but then his papa had died when he was so little a boy that he could not remember very much about him, except that he was big, and had blue eyes and a long mustache, and that it was a splendid thing to be carried around the room on his shoulder. Since his papa's death, Cedric had found out that it was best not to talk to his mamma about him. When his father was ill, Cedric had been sent away, and when he had returned, everything was over; and his mother, who had been very ill, too, was only just beginning to sit in her chair by the window. She was pale and thin, and all the dimples had gone from her pretty face, and her eyes looked large and mournful, and she was dressed in black.

(2) "Dearest," said Cedric (his papa had called her that always, and so the little boy had learned to say it),—"dearest, is my papa better?"

(3) He felt her arms tremble, and so he turned his curly head and looked in her face. There was something in it that made him feel that he was going to cry.

(4) "Dearest," he said, "is he well?"

(5) Then suddenly his loving little heart told him that he'd better put both his arms around her neck and kiss her again and again, and keep his soft cheek close to hers; and he did so, and she laid her face on his shoulder and cried bitterly, holding him as if she could never let him go again.

(6) "Yes, he is well," she sobbed; "he is quite, quite well, but we—we have no one left but each other. No one at all."

(7) Then, little as he was, he understood that his big, handsome young papa would not come back any more; that he was dead, as he had heard of other people being, although he could not comprehend exactly what strange thing had brought all this sadness about. It was because his mamma always cried when he spoke of his papa that he secretly made up his mind it was better not to speak of him very often to her, and he found out, too, that it was better not to let her sit still and look into the fire or out of the window without moving or talking. He and his mamma knew very few people, and lived what might have been thought very lonely lives, although Cedric did not know it was lonely until he grew older and heard why it was they had no visitors. Then he was told that his mamma was an orphan, and quite alone in the world when his papa had married her. She was very pretty, and had been living as companion to a rich old lady who was not kind to her, and one day Captain Cedric Errol, who was calling at the house, saw her run up the stairs with tears on her eyelashes; and she looked so sweet and innocent and sorrowful that the Captain could not forget her. And after many strange things had happened, they knew each other well and loved each other dearly, and were married, although their marriage brought them the ill-will of several persons. The one who was most angry of all, however,

The main idea is the most important point an author makes in a paragraph or in an entire passage. All other information supports the main idea. Sometimes there are multiple main points. As you read, highlight the main idea of every paragraph.

was the Captain's father, who lived in England, and was a very rich and important old nobleman, with a very bad temper and a very violent dislike to America and Americans. He had two sons older than Captain Cedric; and it was the law that the elder of these sons should inherit the family title and estates, which were very rich and splendid; if the eldest son died, the next one would be heir; so, though he was a member of such a great family, there was little chance that Captain Cedric would be very rich himself.

Exercises

1. What are two reasons Cedric calls his mother "Dearest?"

RI.5.5

2. How does paragraph 6 establish the main point or theme of the passage?

RL.5.2

3. What is the narrative point of view in paragraph 7?

A. The reader learns about events in the past through flashbacks.
B. The reader learns about events in the past as they are explained to Cedric.
C. The reader learns about events in the past from the point of view of Cedric's mother.
D. The reader learns about events in the past from the point of view of Cedric's father.

RL.5.6

5. What does the word "comprehend" mean as it is used in this sentence: "Then, little as he was, he understood that his big, handsome young papa would not come back any more; that he was dead, as he had heard of other people being, although he could not comprehend exactly what strange thing had brought all this sadness about."

A. Mourn or grieve
B. Regret or feel bad about having done something
C. Feel angry and confused
D. Understand or make sense of

RL.5.4

4. How does Cedric react to his mother's grief?

A. He tries to comfort her, but generally avoids talking about his father.
B. He asks her questions about his father so he can understand what is going on.
C. He tries to make her feel that everything will be okay.
D. He asks her if he can go away until things are better and it is all over.

RL.5.3

6. Which quote from the text supports the inference that Cedric's mother was beginning to feel better when he returned home and was allowed to see her again?

A. ...and his mother, who had been very ill, too, was only just beginning to sit in her chair by the window.
B. He felt her arms tremble, and so he turned his curly head and looked in her face.
C. Since his papa's death, Cedric had found out that it was best not to talk to his mamma about him.
D. She was pale and thin, and all the dimples had gone from her pretty face, and her eyes looked large and mournful, and she was dressed in black.

RL.5.1

54

WEEK 7

VIDEO
EXPLANATIONS

ARGOPREP.COM

From **A Yankee Girl at Fort Sumter** *By Alice Turner Curtis*

(http://www.gutenberg.org/cache/epub/5696/pg5696-images.html)

(1) "Your name is in a song, isn't it?" said Grace Waite, as she and her new playmate, Sylvia Fulton, walked down the pleasant street on their way to school.

(2) "Is it? Can you sing the song?" questioned Sylvia eagerly, her blue eyes shining at what promised to be such a delightful discovery.

(3) Grace nodded smilingly. She was a year older than Sylvia, nearly eleven years old, and felt that it was quite proper that she should be able to explain to Sylvia more about her name than Sylvia knew herself.

(4) "It is something about 'spelling,'" she explained, and then sang, very softly:

(5) "'Then to Sylvia let us sing,
That Sylvia is spelling.
She excels each mortal thing,
Upon the dull earth dwelling.'

(6) "I suppose it means she was the best speller," Grace said soberly.

(7) "I think it is a lovely song," said Sylvia. "I'll tell my mother about it. I am so glad you told me, Grace."

(8) Sylvia Fulton was ten years old, and had lived in Charleston, South Carolina, for the past year. Before that the Fultons had lived in Boston. Grace Waite lived in the house next to the one which Mr. Fulton had hired in the beautiful southern city, and the two little girls had become fast friends. They both attended Miss Patten's school. Usually Grace's nanny, Esther, escorted them to and from Miss Patten's, but on this morning in early October they were allowed to go by themselves.

(9) As they walked along they could look out across the blue harbor, and see sailing vessels and rowboats coming and going. In the distance were the three forts whose historic names were known to every child in Charleston. Grace never failed to point them out to the little northern girl, and to repeat their names:

(10) "Castle Pinckney," she would say, pointing to the one nearest the city, and then to the long dark forts at the mouth of the harbor, "Fort Sumter, and Fort Moultrie."

(11) "Don't stop to tell me the names of those old forts this morning," said Sylvia. "I know just as much about them now as you do. We shall be late if we don't hurry."

(12) Miss Patten's house stood in a big garden which ran nearly to the water's edge. The schoolroom opened on each side to broad piazzas, and there was always the pleasant fragrance of flowers in the big airy room. Sylvia was sure that no one could be more beautiful than Miss Patten. "She looks just like one of the ladies in your 'Godey's Magazine,'" she had told her mother, on returning home from her first day at school.

Make connections between new information and what you already know. When a passage uses a term you're familiar with, ask yourself if there is new information you can add to your understanding.

(13)   And with her pretty soft black curls, her rosy cheeks and pleasant voice, no one could imagine a more desirable teacher than Miss Rosalie Pattten. There were just twelve little girls in her school. There were never ten, or fourteen. Miss Patten would never engage to take more than twelve pupils; and the twelve always came. Mrs. Waite, Grace's mother, had told Mrs. Fulton that Sylvia was very fortunate to attend the school.

Exercises

1. Based on the information in paragraph 3, the reader can infer...

    A. Sylvia is eager to be Grace's friend.
    B. Grace and Sylvia seldom get to walk to school alone.
    C. Sylvia likes to feel special or unique.
    D. Grace feels superior to Sylvia.

RL.5.1

2. Which quote from the text shows that Grace is eager to get to school?

    A. "She looks just like one of the ladies in your 'Godey's Magazine,'" she had told her mother, on returning home from her first day at school.
    B. Usually Grace's nanny, Esther, escorted them to and from Miss Patten's, but on this morning in early October they were allowed to go by themselves.
    C. "Don't stop to tell me the names of those old forts this morning," said Sylvia.
    D. "I suppose it means she was the best speller," Grace said soberly.

RL.5.2

3. What advantage does Grace feel she has over Sylvia?

    A. She attends Miss Patten's school.
    B. She knows the names of the forts in the harbor.
    C. She has lived in Charleston longer.
    D. Her mother is very beautiful.

RL.5.3

4. In paragraph 5, Grace quotes from the following poem by William Shakespeare. How is her interpretation of the poem different from the original?

Who is Silvia? what is she,
That all our swains commend her?
Holy, fair and wise is she;
The heaven such grace did lend her,
That she might admirèd be.

Is she kind as she is fair?
For beauty lives with kindness.
Love doth to her eyes repair,
To help him of his blindness,
And, being helped, inhabits there.

Then to Silvia let us sing,
That Silvia is excelling;
She excels each mortal thing
Upon the dull earth dwelling:
To her let us garlands bring

    A. Grace believes the poem is about a girl named Silvia or Sylvia, but it is really about nature.
    B. Grace believes the poem is about spelling, but it is really about the beauty of the woman Silvia or Sylvia.
    C. Grace believes the poem is about spelling, but it is really about a ghost or supernatural being.
    D. Grace believes the poem is set in the United States, but it is really set in England.

RL.5.9

From **How it Works** *By Archibald Williams*

(https://www.gutenberg.org/files/28553/28553-h/28553-h.ht)

Why the Wind Blows

(1)   When a child's rubber ball gets slack through a slight leakage of air, and loses some of its bounce, it is a common practice to hold it for a few minutes in front of the fire till it becomes temporarily taut again. Why does the heat have this effect on the ball? No more air has been forced into the ball. It is because the molecules of air dash about more vigorously among one another when the air is heated, and by striking the inside of the ball with greater force put it in a state of greater tension.

(2)   If we heat an open jar there is no pressure developed, since the air simply expands and flows out of the neck. But the air that remains in the jar, being less in quantity than when it was not yet heated, weighs less, though occupying the same space as before. If we took a very thin rubber balloon and filled it with hot air it would therefore float in colder air, proving that heated air, as we should expect, tends to rise. The hot-air-balloon employs this principle, the air inside the bag being kept artificially warm by a fire burning in some vessel attached below the open neck of the bag.

(3)   Now, the sun shines with different degrees of heating power at different parts of the world. Where its effect is greatest the air there is hottest. We will suppose, for the sake of argument, that, at a certain moment, the air envelope all round the globe is of equal temperature. Suddenly the sun shines out and heats the air at a point, a, till it is many degrees warmer than the surrounding air. The heated air expands, rises, and spreads out above the cold air. But, as a given depth of warm air has less weight than an equal depth of cold air, the cold air at once begins to rush towards and squeeze the rest of the warm air out. We may therefore picture the atmosphere as made up of a number of colder currents passing along the surface of the earth to replace warm currents rising and spreading over the upper surface of the cold air. A similar circulation takes place in a vessel of heated water.

LAND AND SEA BREEZES.

(4)   A breeze which blows from the sea on to the land during the day often reverses its direction during the evening. Why is this? The earth grows hot or cold more rapidly than the sea. When the sun shines hotly, the land warms quickly and heats the air over it, which becomes light, and is displaced by the cooler air over the sea. When the sun sets, the earth and the air over it lose their warmth quickly, while the sea remains at practically the same temperature as before. So the balance is changed, the heavier air now lying over the land. It therefore flows seawards, and drives out the warmer air there.

Headings in a text can help you determine the main idea. Try turning a heading into a question. Then as you read the section, find the details necessary to answer the question.

Exercises

1. According to the passage, wind is the result of...

    A. The sun heating the air and land.
    B. Uneven heating and cooling of air and land.
    C. The difference between night and day.
    D. Air over the water moving onto the land.

RI.5.2

4. What evidence does the author provide to show that heated air weighs less than cool air?

    A. He describes an open jar and explains that air can escape from the jar.
    B. He explains why air moves from land to sea when the sun goes down.
    C. He explains how a hot air balloon works.
    D. He explains why a ball seems inflated when you heat it.

RI.5.8

2. How is the experiment with a rubber ball put near a heat source similar to the cause of wind?

    A. Both show that heated air is lighter than colder air.
    B. Both show that air that is contained in something like a ball or balloon is heated faster.
    C. Both show that heated air molecules become active.
    D. Both show that the quantity of air is not as important as the temperature.

RI.5.3

5. What does the author mean when he says "for the sake of argument," in the following excerpt?

"We will suppose, for the sake of argument, that, at a certain moment, the air envelope all round the globe is of equal temperature."

    A. He is simplifying a detail to explain a larger concept.
    B. He knows that many people will disagree with the point he is about to make.
    C. No one can agree on this idea.
    D. He knows the reader is not likely to believe what he's about to say.

RI.5.4

3. This passage has two main sections, "Why the Wind Blows" and "Land and Sea Breezes." The second section mainly....

    A. Provides a different cause of wind currents than is explained in the first section.
    B. Provides an example of cause of wind currents that is explained in the first section.
    C. Simplifies the information from the first section by referring to experiments students can do themselves.
    D. Provides scientific evidence to support the explanation provided in the first section.

RI.5.5

6. A heated "vessel of water" is similar to the air because...

    A. If it is heated enough, it turns to steam, which rises.
    B. It is lighter than cold air.
    C. Currents are created by heat.
    D. Molecules expand.

RI.5.5

From **Makers of Many Things** *By Eva March Tappan PhD*

(https://www.gutenberg.org/files/28569/28569-h/28569-h.htm#THE_DISHES_ON_OUR_TABLES)

The Making of Shoes

(1) Did you ever stop to think how many different qualities you expect in a shoe? You want the sole to be hard and firm so as to protect your feet in rough walking; and also soft and yielding so as to feel springy and not board-like. You want the upper leather to keep the cold air from coming in; and also porous enough to let the perspiration out. Your feet are not exactly like those of any one else; and yet you expect to find at any shoe store a comfortable shoe ready-made. You expect that shoe to come close to your foot, and yet allow you to move it with perfect freedom. You expect all these good qualities, and what is more remarkable, it does not seem difficult for most people to get them. There is an old saying, "To him who wears shoes, the whole earth is covered with leather"; and although many different materials have been tried in shoemaking, leather is the only one that has proved satisfactory, for the sole of the shoe at least. Of late, however, rubber and rubber combinations and felts and felt combinations have been used.

(2) In earlier times the shoemaker used to go from house to house with his lapstone, waxed end, awl, and other tools. The farmer provided the leather, which he had tanned from the hides of his own cattle. Now, however, manufacturers can buy the soles of one merchant, the heels of another, the box toe and stiffenings of another, and so on. In the United States there are many factories which do nothing but cut soles, or rather stamp them out with dies, a hundred or more in a minute. These soles and also the less heavy inner soles go through machines that make all parts of them of a uniform thickness. The traveling shoemaker always hammered his sole leather to make it wear better; but now a moment between very heavy rollers answers the same purpose. Another machine splits the inner sole for perhaps a quarter of an inch all the way around, and thus makes a little lip to which to sew the welt. A number of layers or "lifts" of leather are cemented together for the heel, and are put under heavy pressure.

(3) The upper parts of a shoe, the "uppers," as they are called, are the vamp or front of the shoe, the top, the tip, and (in a laced shoe) the tongue. Nearly all the upper leather that shows when a shoe is on is made from the hides of cattle, calves, goats, and sheep; but besides the parts that show there are stiffeners for the box toe and the counters to support the quarters over the heel; there are linings, and many other necessary "findings," forty-four parts in all in an ordinary shoe. Much experimenting and more thinking have gone into every one of these forty-four parts; and much remembering that shoes have harder wear than anything else in one's wardrobe. The cotton linings, for instance, must be woven in a special way in order to make them last and not "rub up" when they are wet with water or perspiration. They are bleached with the utmost care not to weaken them, and they are singed between red-hot copper plates to remove all the nap.

TIP of the **DAY**

When answering a question that asks you to contrast two things, plan your writing with a chart. Choose two or three criteria, or characteristics, and use information from the text to look at how the characteristics are different.

Exercises

1. How is shoemaking today different from shoemaking in the earlier times?

_____

_____

_____

_____

_____

_____

_____

_____

_____

RI.5.5.

2. Use evidence from the text to explain why it can be difficult to find a shoe that fits well.

_____

_____

_____

_____

_____

_____

_____

_____

RI.5.1

Exercises

3. What does the expression, "To him who wears shoes, the whole earth is covered with leather," mean?

A. Most shoes are made of leather.
B. People should not wear shoes.
C. People who wear shoes walk on leather.
D. Leather is being replaced with felt and rubber for soles of shoes.

RI.5.4

5. What is the main idea of paragraph 3?

A. Shoes are constructed mostly of leather.
B. Shoes generally have leather soles.
C. There are 44 different parts to the average shoe.
D. Every aspect of shoe construction is carefully thought out.

RI.5.2

4. Why are the cotton linings of shoes given so much attention?

A. The lining is the least durable part of the shoe.
B. The lining is created by special factories.
C. The lining is made of cotton.
D. The lining has direct contact with the wearer's foot.

RI.5.9

6. What does "singed" likely mean as it is used in the last sentence of the passage?

A. Burned
B. Sewn
C. Assembled
D. Cut

RI.5.4

WEEK 8

VIDEO
EXPLANATIONS

ARGOPREP.COM

Find detailed video explanations to each problem on:
ArgoPrep.com

From **Fifty Famous People** *By James Baldwin*

(http://www.gutenberg.org/cache/epub/6168/pg6168-images.html)

THE MIDNIGHT RIDE

(1)   The midnight ride of Paul Revere happened a long time ago when this country was ruled by the king of England. There were thousands of English soldiers in Boston. The king had sent them there to make the people obey his unjust laws. These soldiers guarded the streets of the town; they would not let anyone go out or come in without their leave.

(2)   The people did not like this. They said, "We have a right to be free men, but the king treats us as slaves. He makes us pay taxes and gives us nothing in return. He sends soldiers among us to take away our liberty."

(3)   A group of men from all over the area came to help the people of Boston. These men were not afraid of the king's soldiers. Some of them camped in Charlestown, a village near Boston. From the hills of Charlestown they could watch and see what the king's soldiers were doing.

(4)   They wished to be ready to defend themselves against the soldiers, so they bought some gunpowder and stored it at Concord, nearly twenty miles away.

(5)   The king's soldiers heard about this gunpowder, and they made up their minds to go out and get it for themselves.

(6)   Among the watchers at Charlestown was a brave young man named Paul Revere. One day a friend of his who lived in Boston came to see him.

(7)   "Some of the king's soldiers are going to Concord to get the gunpowder that is there. They are getting ready to start this very night."

(8)   "Indeed!" said Paul Revere. "They shall get no powder, if I can help it. I will stir up all the farmers between here and Concord. You must help me."

(9)   "I will do all that I can," said his friend.

(10)   "Well, then," said Paul Revere, "you must go back to Boston and watch. As soon as the soldiers are ready to start, hang a lantern in the tower of the old North Church. If they are to cross the river, hang two. I will be here, ready. As soon as I see the light, I will mount my horse and ride out to give the alarm."

(11)   When night came, Paul Revere was at the riverside with his horse. He looked over toward Boston. He knew where the old North Church stood, but he could not see much in the darkness. Hour after hour he stood and watched.

(12)   The moon rose, and by its light he could see the dim form of the church tower, far away. All at once a light flashed out from the tower. "Ah! there it is!" he cried. The soldiers had started. Then another light flashed clear and bright by the side of the first one. The soldiers would cross the river.

TIP of the DAY

The theme is the overall message or observation about a situation a text makes. Details that support a theme often focus on why characters do things, or the results of characters' actions.

(13) Paul Revere sprang into the saddle. Away they went through the village street and out upon the country road. "Up! up!" shouted Paul Revere. "The soldiers are coming! Up! up! and defend yourselves!"

(14) The cry awoke the farmers; they sprang from their beds and looked out. They understood the cry, "Up! up! and defend yourselves!"

(15) "It is the alarm! The redcoats are coming," they said to each other. Then they took their guns, their axes, anything they could find, and hurried out.

(16) The king's soldiers were surprised to find everybody awake along the road. At Lexington, not far from Concord, there was a sharp fight. This, in history, is called the Battle of Lexington. It was the beginning of the Revolutionary War. The king's soldiers did not find the gunpowder. They were glad enough to march back without it. All along the road the farmers were waiting for them. It seemed as if every man in the country was after them.

Exercises

1. Which quote from the text best supports the author's claim that England was interfering with the freedom of colonists in America?

A. A group of men from all over the area came to help the people of Boston. These men were not afraid of the king's soldiers.
B. He makes us pay taxes and gives us nothing in return.
C. The king's soldiers were surprised to find everybody awake along the road. At Lexington, not far from Concord, there was a sharp fight.
D. "Some of the king's soldiers are going to Concord to get the gunpowder that is there. They are getting ready to start this very night."

RI.5.1

2. Which statement best describes the narrator of this passage?

A. A first person account of an historical event.
B. A third person account of an historical event.
C. A second person account of an historical event.
D. A third person account of a fictional event.

RI.5.6

3. How did encountering the colonists along the road change the attitudes of the British soldiers?

A. The soldiers gave up their mission and focused on getting back to Boston safely.
B. The soldiers became resentful that the colonists were interfering with their mission.
C. The soldiers realized they were going to lose the Revolutionary War.
D. The soldiers became concerned about the people of Boston, whom they'd mistreated.

RI.5.3

4. How does the following excerpt support the theme of the text, "A group of men from all over the area came to help the people of Boston. These men were not afraid of the king's soldiers."

A. It shows that the colonists were much braver than the British soldiers.
B. It demonstrates the importance of communication during times of war.
C. It shows that the problems faced by Boston were important to the entire colony.
D. It demonstrates that planning is as important as taking action in times of trouble.

RI.5.2

Find detailed video explanations to each problem on:
ArgoPrep.com

Striking Out for Themselves *By F.H. Sweet*

(https://www.gutenberg.org/files/27287/27287-h/27287-h.htm)

(1)　"Reckon we'll get 'em burned out by Tuesday week, Tom, and be ready for Pylant's oranges. Suppose the old fellow will want us to take pay in town lots, though."

(2)　"He'll get left if he does;" and the lad by the fire removed the skillet of fried bacon from the coals and put the coffee-pot in its place. "I'm willing to work out a five-acre lot, but don't want any towns. Say, Dave, what do you think of the party going to Punta Rassa?" he added, as he thrust a stick into the bean-pot to see what prospect there was for an early supper.

(3)　"Well, from what I hear, I fancy there is plenty of good land to be homesteaded in that section, and if we didn't have a good job here, I'd be for joining them. I begin to feel a little anxious to have some land where we can be starting trees of our own."

(4)　"Same here," said Tom, "but the land will come in good time, and while we've got a week's rations of bacon and hominy ahead, I shan't kick against luck. But grub's ready."

(5)　Both lads fell to with a relish. Beans seemed to be the central dish at almost every meal, and yet they somehow never seemed to tire of them.

(6)　They had encountered a good many hard knocks since leaving their Western home, but were evidently none the worse for them.

(7)　Dave Freeman, the son of a hard-working Kansas farmer, had come South to better his prospects, and with a deep but unexpressed longing to help the home folks.

(8)　At Flomaton, or Pensacola Junction, as it is now called, he had fallen in with Tom Byrne, an Indiana boy, and the two had soon become fast friends.

(9)　By getting occasional jobs along the way, and not infrequently "tramping it," they had reached their present quarters, near Panasofkee, in Sumter County.

(10)　Here they had taken a contract from a "papertown" proprietor to clear five acres of land for seventy-five dollars.

(11)　This was a low figure, as the ground was full of palmetto roots, and not only were the trees to be cleared from the land, but all stumps to be burned out.

(12)　The boys already had been at work over two months, and hoped that another week would complete the job. On the first, their employer was to commence gathering his oranges, and they expected several weeks' employment with him.

(13)　Although the work of clearing was very hard, the boys were rugged and hearty, and thoroughly enjoyed their novel surroundings.

The setting of a story includes the time and place. As you read, annotate the text to make note of details that tell you about the setting.

(14) After finishing their beans, they put away the few dishes, and began the round of their stumps. Here and there one was dying out, and new fuel had to be piled around it. As one stump burned out, it was dragged from its hole and placed against the roots of another.

(15) A few days before the boys finished their contract, a party of surveyors stopped at their shanty to get a drink of water, and to see if they could get them for a couple of days.

(16) As the pay offered was good, the boys were glad to accept it, and five minutes were sufficient to put their few belongings into the shanty and to nail up the door.

(17) It took the party some hours to reach their destination, and as soon as they had partaken of a lunch, they began to survey a site for a new town.

(18) The boys had seen a great many "paper towns" since they came to Florida, but as a rule had taken little interest in them. They were usually ventures of men who did not have money enough to make their speculations a success.

Exercises

1. Why did the boys leave their first job clearing land to take a second job surveying another parcel of land?

   A. They had completed clearing the stumps from the land for their first job.
   B. The second job would not take long and paid well.
   C. They did not believe they would be paid in cash for the first job.
   D. They wanted to set up a homestead for themselves.
   RL.5.1

2. What is Tom's reaction to Dave's interest in getting land of his own?

   A. Tom disagrees with Dave and doesn't think it is worthwhile for them to try to "homestead" or get their own land.
   B. Tom agrees, but feels they need to have more money for their basic needs before they buy land.
   C. Tom agrees, but believes they should each have their own homesteads and own investments.
   D. Tom disagrees because he wants to send any money he makes back to his family in Indiana.
   RL.5.2

3. What is one way this story would be different if it were told from Dave's point of view?

   A. It might include more details about the family he left behind and his plans to help them.
   B. It might include more details about the work the boys are doing in clearing the stumps.
   C. It might include more information about the "paper towns" that both Dave and Tom refer to.
   D. It might include Tom's impressions or ideas about Dave's goals in working toward owning his own land.
   RL.5.5

4. What is the purpose of paragraph 5 in this passage?

   A. To show that the boys always took a break for lunch.
   B. To show that the boys were poor, but enthusiastic about their work.
   C. To show that the boys were struggling to survive on their own.
   D. To show that the boys needed to earn more money in order to reach their goals.
   RL.5.6

 Find detailed video explanations to each problem on:
ArgoPrep.com

The Forests of the White Mountains. *By F. Parkman*

(https://www.gutenberg.org/files/32141/32141-h/32141-h.htm)

(1)   New Hampshire is not a particularly wealthy state, but it has some resources scarcely equaled by those of any of its sisters. The White Mountains, though worth little to the farmer, are a piece of real estate which yields a sure and abundant income by attracting tourists and their money; and this revenue is certain to increase, unless blind mismanagement interferes. The White Mountains are at present unique objects of attraction; but they may easily be spoiled, and the yearly tide of tourists could be turned to other points of interest – those that are not spoiled by development.

(2)   The reason these mountains are so spectacular is that they are covered with dense, ancient forests, which have never been cut. Speculators, or people who invest in land hoping to sell its resources, have their eyes these forests. If they are permitted to have their way, the state will find that a valuable resource could suddenly and permanently become worthless. If the mountains are robbed of their forests they will become like some other mountains in the world, such as the Pyrenees. The Pyrenees are a mountain range dividing Spain and France. They were once covered in beautiful forests, and attracted tourists and hikers. However, speculators were allowed to cut these forests, leaving only rocky, unattractive and dangerous hills and cliffs. The mountains were no longer suited for visitors.

(3)   The forests of the White Mountains have a considerable commercial value; they are worth a lot of money. This great value need not be sacrificed. When lumber speculators get possession of forests they generally cut down all the trees and strip the land at once, with an eye to immediate profit. There is another way. The more conservative, and, in the end, the more profitable management, consists in selecting and cutting out the valuable timber when it has matured. Smart lumber investors leave the younger growth of trees for future use. This process is not very harmful to the landscape. It is practiced extensively in Maine. In Maine expert land and lumber investors have mastered the art of using forests wisely. A fair amount of good lumber may thus be drawn from the White Mountains, without hurting their value as the permanent source of a vastly greater income from the attraction they will offer to an increasing influx of tourists. At the same time the streams flowing from them, and especially the Pemigewasset River, a main source of the Merrimac River, will be saved from the alternate droughts and floods to which all streams are exposed that take their rise in mountains denuded of forests. All the mill owners along these rivers and streams rely on their consistent flow. If there are floods, or if a drought dries up these rivers, many businesses will suffer.

 **TIP** of the **DAY**

Authors write to inform, to entertain, and to persuade. Texts written to entertain are usually stories, poems, or plays. Informative texts tell the reader how to do something or describe and explain an idea or location. A persuasive text tries to convince the reader to agree with a certain point of view.

Exercises

1. What is the main idea of paragraph 2 of this passage?

RI.5.2

2. Why did the author most likely write this passage?

RI.5.1

Exercises

3. What is the point of the comparison the author makes in paragraph 2, between The White Mountains and the Pyrenees?

A. To show that the two mountain ranges are of similar size and in similar climates.
B. To show how well-maintained forests can attract long term income from tourists.
C. To show what could happen if the forests of the White Mountains are not protected.
D. To show that countries all over the world face similar challenges.

RI.5.3

5. What new point of view is introduced in paragraph 3 to provide more support for the author's argument that the forests should be preserved?

A. The point of view of land speculators who need the wood to earn money
B. The point of view of lumber investors in Maine who are concerned about the forests in New Hampshire.
C. The point of view of tourists, who enjoy spending time in the forests of New Hampshire.
D. The point of view of mill owners, who rely on the rivers that run from the White Mountains.

RI.5.6

4. In this sentence from paragraph 1, which definition best fits how the word "tide" is used?

"The White Mountains are at present unique objects of attraction; but they may easily be spoiled, and the yearly tide of tourists could be turned to other points of interest – those that are not spoiled by development."

A. Rising and falling of the sea along the beach
B. A powerful surge of feeling
C. A large group of people moving together
D. Drifting aimlessly, as though floating on water

RI.5.4

6. What cause/effect relationship is described in paragraph 3 of this passage?

A. Cutting only mature trees will cause an increase in tourism in the White Mountains.
B. Destroying the forests of the White Mountains will cause droughts and floods.
C. The way forests are managed in Maine will cause tourists to visit Maine rather than the White Mountains in New Hampshire.
D. Mills and factories along the rivers will cause droughts and floods.

RI.5.5

WEEK 9

VIDEO
EXPLANATIONS

ARGOPREP.COM

From **Cocoa and Chocolate: Their History from Plantation to Consumer**
By Arthur W. Knapp

(https://www.gutenberg.org/files/19073/19073-h/19073-h.htm#chapter1)

Montezuma—the First Great Patron of Chocolate.

(1)   When Columbus discovered the New World he brought back with him to Europe many new and curious things, one of which was cacao. Some years later, in 1519, the Spanish conquistador, Cortes, landed in Mexico, marched into the interior and discovered to his surprise, not the huts of savages, but a beautiful city, with palaces and museums. This city was the capital of the Aztecs, a remarkable people, notable alike for their ancient civilization and their wealth. Their national drink was chocolate. Montezuma, their Emperor, who lived in a state of luxurious magnificence, "took no other beverage than the chocolatl, a potation of chocolate, flavored with vanilla and other spices, and so prepared as to be reduced to a froth of the consistency of honey, which gradually dissolved in the mouth and was taken cold. This beverage if you could call it that, was served in golden goblets, with spoons of the same metal or tortoise-shell finely wrought. The Emperor was exceedingly fond of it, to judge from the quantity—no less than fifty jars or pitchers being prepared for his own daily consumption: two thousand more were allowed for that of his household." It is curious that Montezuma drank no other beverage than chocolate. How long this ancient people, students of the mysteries of culinary science, had known the art of preparing a drink from cacao, is not known, but it is evident that the cultivation of cacao received great attention in these parts, for if we read down the list of the tributes paid by different cities to the Lords of Mexico, we find "20 chests of ground chocolate, 20 bags of gold dust," again "80 loads of red chocolate, 20 lip-jewels of clear amber," and yet again "200 loads of chocolate."

(2)   Another people that share with the Aztecs the honor of being the first great cultivators of cacao are the Incas of Peru, that wonderful nation that knew not poverty.

The Fascination of Chocolate.

(3)   That chocolate charmed the ladies of Mexico in the seventeenth century (even as it charms the ladies of England to-day) is shown by a story which Gage relates in his New Survey of the West Indias (1648). He tells us that at Chiapa, southward from Mexico, the women used to interrupt church services by having their maids bring them a cup of hot chocolate; and when the Bishop, after fair warning, scolded them, or spoke sharply to them for their behavior, they changed their church.

Cacao Beans as Money.

(4)   Cacao was used by the Aztecs not only for the preparation of a beverage, but also as a form of money. For example, one could purchase a "tolerably good cart" for 100 beans. We read that: "Their currency consisted of transparent quills of gold dust, of bits of tin cut in the form of a T, and of bags of cacao containing a specified number of grains." "Blessed money," exclaims Peter Martyr, "which exempts its possessor from greed, since it spoils and cannot be long hoarded, nor hidden underground!"

When answering an inference question, review the answer choices and use the information from the passage to narrow your choices. Search for details to support each answer. If the details are not in the passage, eliminate the answer choice and move on to the next.

Exercises

1. What inference can you make from paragraph 2 and the author's decision to include this information?

   A. The Aztecs were inspired by the Incas of Peru.
   B. The Aztecs and Incas were once very poor civilizations.
   C. Cultivating cacao led to wealth.
   D. Only wealthy civilizations could afford chocolate.

   RI.5.1

2. What theme is supported by paragraph 3 of this passage?

   A. Obsession or fascination can lead to poor choices and bad behavior.
   B. Refusing to follow rules and customs has negative consequences.
   C. Eating too much chocolate causes problems.
   D. Great wealth is not always a good thing.

   RI.5.2

3. How were Columbus and Cortes alike?

   A. Both explored great Mexican cities.
   B. Both saw how important cacao was in the new world.
   C. Both used cacao as currency with the native people of the new world.
   D. Both found great Aztec cities.

   RI.5.3

4. What does the phrase "knew not poverty" mean as it is used in paragraph 2?

   A. Were poor because they didn't realize the value of their natural resources.
   B. Were poor, but did not know it, as they had all they needed.
   C. Were wealthy, but caused others to live in poverty.
   D. Were wealthy and had never known poverty or been poor.

   RI.5.4

5. In paragraph 4, the author quotes Peter Martyr. What does Martyr see as a great benefit of using cacao as money?

   A. It is plentiful and can be cultivated or grown.
   B. It can be made into delicious beverages.
   C. It spoils or goes bad, so it must be spent or shared with others.
   D. If it spoils or goes bad, it is easy to get more.

   RI.5.6

6. Which quote provides evidence for the author's claim that cacao was valued throughout Mexico and the surrounding region?

   A. for if we read down the list of the tributes paid by different cities to the Lords of Mexico, we find "20 chests of ground chocolate, 20 bags of gold dust,"
   B. This beverage if you could call it that, was served in golden goblets, with spoons of the same metal or tortoise-shell finely wrought.
   C. Montezuma, their Emperor, who lived in a state of luxurious magnificence, "took no other beverage than the chocolatl, a potation of chocolate...
   D. Some years later, in 1519, the Spanish conquistador, Cortes, landed in Mexico, marched into the interior and discovered to his surprise, not the huts of savages, but a beautiful city, with palaces and museums.

   RI.5.8

Find detailed video explanations to each problem on:
ArgoPrep.com

THE CAPTURE OF FATHER TIME *By L. Frank Baum*

(https://www.gutenberg.org/files/4357/4357-h/4357-h.htm#capture)

(1)   Jim was the son of a cowboy, and lived on the broad plains of Arizona. His father had trained him to lasso a bronco or a young bull with perfect accuracy, and had Jim possessed the strength to back up his skill he would have been as good a cowboy as any in all Arizona.

(2)   When he was twelve years old he made his first visit to the east, where Uncle Charles, his father's brother, lived. Of course Jim took his lasso with him, for he was proud of his skill in casting it, and wanted to show his cousins what a cowboy could do.

(3)   At first the city boys and girls were much interested in watching Jim lasso posts and fence pickets, but they soon tired of it, and even Jim decided it was not the right sort of sport for cities.

(4)   But one day the butcher asked Jim to ride one of his horses into the country, to a pasture that had been engaged, and Jim eagerly consented. He had been longing for a horseback ride, and to make it seem like old times he took his lasso with him.

(5)   He rode through the streets demurely enough, but on reaching the open country roads his spirits broke forth into wild jubilation, and, urging the butcher's horse to full gallop, he dashed away in true cowboy fashion.

(6)   Then he wanted still more liberty, and letting down the bars that led into a big field he began riding over the meadow and throwing his lasso at imaginary cattle, while he yelled and whooped to his heart's content.

(7)   Suddenly, on making a long cast with his lasso, the loop caught upon something and rested about three feet from the ground, while the rope drew taut and nearly pulled Jim from his horse.

(8)   This was unexpected. More than that, it was wonderful; for the field seemed bare of even a stump. Jim's eyes grew big with amazement, but he knew he had caught something when a voice cried out:

(9)   "Here, let go! Let go, I say! Can't you see what you've done?"

(10)   No, Jim couldn't see, nor did he intend to let go until he found out what was holding the loop of the lasso. So he resorted to an old trick his father had taught him and, putting the butcher's horse to a run, began riding in a circle around the spot where his lasso had caught.

(11)   As he thus drew nearer and nearer his quarry he saw the rope coil up, yet it looked to be coiling over nothing but air. One end of the lasso was made fast to a ring in the saddle, and when the rope was almost wound up and the horse began to pull away and snort with fear, Jim dismounted. Holding the reins of the bridle in one hand, he followed the rope, and an instant later saw an old man caught fast in the coils of the lasso.

(12)   While Jim gazed wonderingly upon him, this venerable old man spoke in an angry voice:

(13)   "Now, then—get that rope off as fast as you can! You've brought everything on earth to a standstill by your

Direct text questions ask for information you find right in the text. When answering a direct text question, don't rely on memory; go back to the text and confirm your answer.

foolishness! Well—what are you staring at? Don't you know who I am?"

(14)   "No," said Jim, stupidly.

(15)   "Well, I'm Time—Father Time! Now, make haste and set me free—if you want the world to run properly."

(16)   "How did I happen to catch you?" asked Jim, without making a move to release his captive.

(17)   "I don't know. I've never been caught before," growled Father Time. "But I suppose it was because you were foolishly throwing your lasso at nothing."

(18)   "I didn't see you," said Jim.

(19)   "Of course you didn't. I'm invisible to the eyes of human beings unless they get within three feet of me, and I take care to keep more than that distance away from them. That's why I was crossing this field, where I supposed no one would be.

Exercises

1. Which excerpt from the text best supports the idea that Jim sometimes wished he was back home in Arizona?

   A. ... and had Jim possessed the strength to back up his skill he would have been as good a cowboy as any in all Arizona.
   B. and had Jim possessed the strength to back up his skill he would have been as good a cowboy as any in all Arizona.
   C. At first the city boys and girls were much interested in watching Jim lasso posts and fence pickets, but they soon tired of it...
   D. He had been longing for a horseback ride, and to make it seem like old times he took his lasso with him.

   RL.5.1

2. Why was Jim able to lasso Father Time, even though the old man was invisible?

   A. Jim was very skilled with his lasso, and could capture even the fastest creatures.
   B. Jim was throwing his lasso at nothing and caught the old man by mistake.
   C. Jim was riding his horse so fast that he caught up with Father Time.
   D. Jim was riding with his eyes closed, so Father Time didn't hide from him.

   RL.5.1

3. What details from the text show the reader how Father Time felt after Jim lassoed him?

   A. Jim dismounted. Holding the reins of the bridle in one hand, he followed the rope, and an instant later saw an old man caught fast in the coils of the lasso.
   B. Well—what are you staring at? Don't you know who I am?" "No," said Jim, stupidly.
   C. "Well, I'm Time—Father Time! Now, make haste and set me free—if you want the world to run properly."
   D. "I don't know. I've never been caught before," growled Father Time. "But I suppose it was because you were foolishly throwing your lasso at nothing."

   RL.5.2

4. What change occurs in Jim in paragraph 5?

   A. He gave up acting like a cowboy because he knew it wasn't the right way to behave in the city.
   B. He gave up his polite city behavior and became a happy, excited cowboy again.
   C. He remembered how much he missed Arizona and decided to run away and go back there.
   D. He realized he couldn't pretend to behave according to the rules of the city anymore and decided to be himself.

   RL.5.3

A Visit to a Farm Adapted from: Rural Hours by Susan Fenimore Cooper

(http://www.worldcat.org/title/rural-hours/oclc/3339732/editions?start_edition=21&sd=desc&referer=di&se=yr&editionsView=true&fq=)

(1) In 1850 Susan Fenimore Cooper, the daughter of a well-known author, wrote about visiting a rural farm. Susan was also a successful author. She was fascinated by rural life. She had great respect for farmers and their wives, whom she considered self-sufficient.

(2) Susan considered the 1850s a very modern time. In 1844 Elias Howe had invented the sewing machine. Clothing became less expensive. Great factories sprung up along the east coast. Clothing was made quickly and inexpensively. People were moving to towns and cities and finding work in factories or shops. With the money they earned they purchased items from the same factories and shops, making them rely on businesses for every aspect of their lives. Americans were becoming less self-sufficient.

(3) Susan visited the farm hoping to learn more about how farmers and country people lived. One of the first things that caught her attention was a "great spinning-wheel" in the corner of the great room of the farmhouse. She learned that the women of the family used the wheel to turn wool from the sheep they raised into yarn. The women then used that yarn to knit socks and weave cloth. The farmer's wife explained how she once had six step-daughters who helped with spinning, dying the yarn, knitting, and weaving cloth. The step-daughters had married or gone to work in the factories. The farmer's wife hired local women to help her.

(4) Susan was amazed. All of the family's clothing, their bed sheets, their towels, and their blankets were made by hand. They needed no more than twelve dollars a year to buy the raw materials such as thread, sewing needles, or ribbons for some of the clothes. "The wives and daughters of our farmers," said Susan, "are very notable, frugal women." Susan believed they were very different from the young women who lived in more populated areas. She thought the young women of the cities were "wildly extravagant." Those who worked, she said, "often spend all they earn in finery." Because they worked in the city, they could no longer create their own clothing. It is ironic, of course, that young women would leave their self-sufficient homes to work for wages, only to spend those wages on what they might have made themselves if they'd remained at home.

Age of workers in cotton mills in Lancashire 1833		
Age	Male	Female
under 11	246	155
11 - 16	1,169	1,123
17 - 21	736	1,240
22 - 26	612	780
27 - 31	355	295
32 - 36	215	100
37 - 41	168	81
42 - 56	98	38
47 - 51	88	23
52 - 56	41	4
57 - 61	28	3

When reviewing charts, pay attention to the title, which tells you what information is included, and column headings, which sort the information. Look for trends in each column, and compare information between rows.

Exercises

1. What did Susan find amazing about the farms she visited?

RI.5.2

2. According to this passage, how are young women in the city different from those in the country?

RI.5.3

3. The chart can best be used to provide the reader with information about...

A. The ages of women working in the factories.
B. The reasons why women left farms to work in factories.
C. Evidence to show that men earned more than women in factories.
D. Evidence to show that women often left factories because of injuries.

RI.5.7

4. Which excerpt from the text best supports the inference that Susan did not think it was a good idea for young women to leave farms and go to work in factories?

A. "The wives and daughters of our farmers," said Susan, "are very notable, frugal women."
B. She had great respect for farmers and their wives, whom she considered self-sufficient.
C. The farmer's wife explained how she once had six step-daughters who helped with spinning, dying the yarn, knitting, and weaving cloth.
D. It is ironic, of course, that young women would leave their self-sufficient homes to work for wages, only to spend those wages on what they might have made themselves if they'd remained at home.

RI.5.1

5. According to the chart, in what age group were most of the women working in these factories?

A. Under 11 to 16
B. 11-26
C. 17-26
D. 22-36

RI.5.7

6. What does the word "frugal" most likely mean as it is used in paragraph 4?

A. Hard working
B. Poor
C. Careful with money
D. Self-reliant (or independent)

RI.5.4

WEEK 10

VIDEO
EXPLANATIONS

ARGOPREP.COM

Find detailed video explanations to each problem on:
ArgoPrep.com

Cousin Charlie's Visit *By F. Clifton Bingham*

(https://www.gutenberg.org/files/17750/17750-h/17750-h.htm)

(1) "I have a surprise for you, dears," said mother, coming into the nursery one morning, followed by a bright-looking boy about ten years of age. "Here is your Cousin Charlie come to spend the day with you."

(2) Dolly and May were delighted, and Mother said they might stay out all the morning. For the first hour they were very happy—there were so many new things to show Charlie; but he was one of those restless boys who get tired of everything very quickly.

(3) "What shall we do next?" he kept saying. They tried hunting for eggs in the barn, but he soon called that "slow."

(4) "Let's go and pick blackberries in the upper field," said little May.

(5) So they started off and had only picked a very little while when Charlie suddenly asked: "Whose orchard is that just across the next field?"

(6) "It's Farmer Giles's," said Dolly.

(7) "Let's climb over and get some apples," was his next idea.

(8) Dolly and May opened their eyes very wide. "That would be stealing," they cried, both together.

(9) "Nonsense," said Charlie. "That's just like girls—always afraid to do anything. I mean to get a pocketful, so you can wait till I come back."

(10) They waited and waited such a long time, but he never came, so they went slowly home. It was nearly tea-time when the nanny came and said: "Farmer Giles has brought Cousin Charlie back." And a very miserable-looking boy he was.

(11) When he had filled his pockets and meant to come down, he saw Rover, the savage farm dog, waiting for him below; so he had to stay in the tree, and might have had to remain all night, only the farmer happened to ride by and heard the dog barking.

(12) Dolly and May were very sorry for him, and their mother did not scold him as she meant to do, because, she said, "the fright had been punishment enough."

Many words have multiple definitions. The definitions are used in different contexts. To determine the correct definition for a word, be sure to consider the context – or the sentence and paragraph in which it is used.

Exercises

1. What part of the story is illustrated in the image?

   A. Cousin Charlie arriving for a visit.
   B. Cousin Charlie leaving after his visit.
   C. Farmer Giles bringing Charlie home.
   D. Dolly and May's mother deciding not to scold Charlie.

RL.5.7

4. What is the meaning of the word "savage" as it is used in paragraph 11?

   A. Ferocious and dangerous
   B. Rugged and strong
   C. Uncivilized and primitive
   D. Something that is very severe or damaging

RL.5.4

2. Which excerpt from the text shows the reader that the girls were shocked by Charlie's idea that they should go into the orchard?

   A. but he was one of those restless boys who get tired of everything very quickly.
   B. "Let's climb over and get some apples," was his next idea.
   C. Dolly and May opened their eyes very wide.
   D. They waited and waited such a long time, but he never came, so they went slowly home.

RL.5.1

5. What can the reader tell about the setting of the story based on paragraphs 2-5?

   A. It is quiet and very well maintained so that all of the buildings are safe and clean.
   B. It is a farm where people have animals and fields for animals.
   C. It is a large home near town where people know their neighbors.
   D. It is a farm near the home of Dolly and May, possibly belonging to their neighbors.

RL.5.3

3. What information is left out by the narrator of this story?

   A. What Charlie wanted to do in the orchard.
   B. How the girls felt when Charlie arrived for his visit.
   C. How the girls' mother reacted when Charlie was returned.
   D. What the girls told their mother and nanny when they came home for tea without Charlie.

RL.5.6

6. What lesson does Charlie learn in this story?

   A. Farms can be dangerous places.
   B. Rushing from one activity to the next is never a good idea.
   C. Boys should listen to girls more often.
   D. There are consequences for breaking rules.

RL.5.9

Bathing a Dog *By Jill Mountain*

(1) Many people have heard the expression that a dog is man's best friend. Unfortunately, there are times when man's best friend gets into something he shouldn't have and, as a result, needs a bath. Some dogs are water-lovers and relish a chance to splash around. Others, however, must be convinced to sit still long enough to be cleaned up. These instructions should make it somewhat easier to wash the grime from a four-legged friend.

(2) According to the television personality known as the "Dog Whisperer," the first step toward having a positive dog-bathing experience is to establish a positive attitude. "Make peace in your head," advises Caesar Millan, "that bathing the dog is a necessity." Caesar Millan claims that dogs can sense a human's apprehension and, if the human helping him bathe is nervous, the dog will be nervous too.

(3) Once you're in the right state of mind, gather together everything you'll need for Rover's bath time. Put a non-stick bath mat on the bottom of the tub. This will keep him from slipping and potentially injuring himself. Make sure you have shampoo and some sort of container for pouring water. Add enough lukewarm water to the tub to completely cover the dog's feet and the lower part of his legs. The dog should not be in the room while you're making preparations, as he may grow anxious.

(4) Once the bath is prepared, it is time to collect the dog. Use a leash and your normal, firm, tone of voice. Walk the dog to the bath the same way you'd walk him in any other situation.

(5) Begin by wetting the dog down with a gentle stream of water. You can increase the water pressure as he grows more comfortable with the situation. Once he is completely wet, begin shampooing the coat, starting at the neck and shoulders. Work your way, with shampoo, down the length of the dog's body. Leave the face for last.

(6) Be sure that you rinse every inch of your dog thoroughly. Doing so may require fluffing or back brushing his fur. Any shampoo residue could cause a skin irritation, so make every effort to rinse until the water runs clear and no soap bubbles run from his coat.

(7) Once your dog is washed and rinsed, towel him off thoroughly. He will shake his body vigorously to release water trapped in his coat, so be prepared for a spray of water. It is best to keep your dog in the house for a few hours after a bath, as some dogs try to roll in dirt immediately in order to remove any scents from shampoo or cleansers.

(8) If you bathe a dog regularly, it will eventually become part of his routine, and will no longer be a challenge or stressful experience.

Texts that instruct give the reader information in a specific order. When reading a text that tells you how to do something, annotate by making a short list of steps as you read.

Exercises

1. The author's purpose in writing this text was to....

   A. Entertain with a story about a dog
   B. Describe a process
   C. Inform about different ways to wash dogs
   D. Reflect on her last experience washing a dog

RI.5.1

2. What is the main idea of paragraph 2?

   A. Dogs can understand people's moods
   B. Cesar Millan is a well-known dog expert who offers good advice.
   C. It is important to be calm and positive while washing a dog.
   D. All dogs are nervous around water.

RI.5.2

3. According to the article, why do recently washed dogs try to roll in dirt?

   A. Dogs use the dirt to help dry themselves off.
   B. Dogs prefer to be outside when they are wet.
   C. Dogs don't like the smell of shampoos used to wash them
   D. Dogs enjoy baths and sometimes get dirty so they need to be bathed.

RI.5.3

4. What is the meaning of the word "vigorously" as it is used in paragraph 7?

   A. In a way that is sloppy or messy
   B. With a lot of energy
   C. Showing fear or disgust
   D. Carefully to avoid making a mess

RL.5.4

5. Which of the following should come first in bathing a dog?

   A. Wet the dog gently with lukewarm water.
   B. Shampoo the dog's body
   C. Shampoo the dog's face
   D. Put enough water in a tub to cover the dog's feet and lower legs.

RL.5.5

6. What is paragraph 4 mostly about?

   A. How to get the dog into the tub.
   B. How to talk to a dog.
   C. The basics of walking a dog from one place to another.
   D. How to prepare for the dog's bath before getting the dog.

RL.5.9

Excerpt from **The Railway Children** *By E. Nesbit*

(http://www.gutenberg.org/files/1874/1874-h/1874-h.htm)

(1)   There was always enough to eat, and they wore the same kind of nice clothes they had always worn.

(2)   But in June came three wet days; the rain came down, straight as lances, and it was very, very cold. Nobody could go out, and everybody shivered. They all went up to the door of Mother's room and knocked.

(3)   "Well, what is it?" asked Mother from inside.

(4)   "Mother," said Bobbie, "mayn't I light a fire? I do know how."

(5)   And Mother said: "No, my ducky-love. We mustn't have fires in June—coal is so dear. If you're cold, go and have a good romp in the attic. That'll warm you."

(6)   "But, Mother, it only takes such a very little coal to make a fire."

(7)   "It's more than we can afford, chickeny-love," said Mother, cheerfully. "Now run away, there's darlings—I'm madly busy!"

(8)   "Mother's always busy now," said Phyllis, in a whisper to Peter. Peter did not answer. He shrugged his shoulders. He was thinking.

(9)   After tea they went back to the attic and Peter said to his sisters:—

(10) "I have an idea."

(11) "What's that?" they asked politely.

(12) It was some time before he could be induced to say anything, and when he did it wasn't much. He said:—"The only reason why I won't tell you my idea that I'm going to do is because it MAY be wrong, and I don't want to drag you into it."

(13) "Don't you do it if it's wrong, Peter," said Bobbie; "let me do it." But Phyllis said:—"I should like to do wrong if YOU'RE going to!"

(14) "No," said Peter, rather touched by this devotion; "it's a forlorn hope, and I'm going to lead it. All I ask is that if Mother asks where I am, you won't blab."

(15) "We haven't got anything TO blab," said Bobbie, indignantly.

(16) "If Mother asks where I am, say I'm playing at mines."

(17) "What sort of mines?"

(18) "You just say mines."

It can be difficult to keep track of multiple characters in a short story. Annotate a text by adding notes about each character's actions or traits. Use single words or very short phrases.

(19)   "You might tell US, Pete."

(20)   "If I find a coal-mine, you shall help cart the coal," Peter condescended to promise.

(21)   Two nights after the dawning of Peter's idea he beckoned the girls mysteriously at this twilight hour.

(22)   "Come hither with me," he said, "and bring the baby carriage – our Roman chariot."

(23)   Just above the station many rocks have pushed their heads out through the turf as though they, like the children, were interested in the railway. In a little hollow between three rocks lay a heap of dried brambles and heather.

(24)   Peter halted, turned over the brushwood with a well-scarred boot, and said:– "Here's the first coal from the St. Peter's Mine. We'll take it home in the chariot. Punctuality and despatch. All orders carefully attended to. Any shaped lump cut to suit regular customers."

(25)   The chariot was packed full of coal. And when it was packed it had to be unpacked again because it was so heavy that it couldn't be got up the hill by the three children.

(26)   Three journeys had to be made before the coal from Peter's mine was added to the heap of Mother's coal in the cellar. Afterwards Peter went out alone, and came back very black and mysterious.

(27)   It was a week later that Mrs. Viney remarked to Mother how well this last lot of coal was holding out.

(28)   The children hugged themselves and each other in complicated wriggles of silent laughter as they listened on the stairs. They had all forgotten by now that there had ever been any doubt in Peter's mind as to whether coal-mining was wrong.

Exercises

1. What do the children find so funny in paragraph 28 of the passage?

RL.5.1

2. Although the narrator does not specifically say, what can the reader infer about the family described in this passage?

_____

_____

_____

_____

_____

_____

_____

_____

RL.5.1

3. Paragraph 28, at the end of the story, suggests what is missing from this story?

A. The consequences the children face when people discover what they did.
B. A description of how much warmer and more comfortable the house became.
C. Important details about the relationship between Mrs. Viney and the children's mother.
D. Peter's own reaction to his mother's surprise at how long the coal has lasted.

RL.5.5

5. What does the word "induced" mean as it is used in this sentence, "It was some time before he could be induced to say anything, and when he did it wasn't much."

A. Argued
B. Forced
C. Coaxed
D. Required

RL.5.4

4. How might the story be different if Peter were the narrator?

A. The reader would learn more about the circumstances of the family and why the children's mother was always so busy.
B. The reader would learn more about where the coal came from and why it might be "wrong" to take it.
C. The reader would learn more about other, similar adventures the children had undertaken and how they worked out.
D. The reader would learn more about why Mrs. Viney frequently visited their home.

RL.5.6

6. What problem did Peter solve by the end of this story?

A. He solved the problem of the family having less money than it used to.
B. He solved the problem of his mother always being too busy for the children.
C. He solved the problem of the family having to careful about heating the house.
D. He solved the problem of whether or not his plan was wrong.

RL.5.2

WEEK 11

VIDEO
EXPLANATIONS

ARGOPREP.COM

Find detailed video explanations to each problem on:
ArgoPrep.com

AN EVENTFUL JOURNEY. From Golden Moments: Bright Stories for Young Folks

(https://www.gutenberg.org/files/22308/22308-h/22308-h.htm)

(1) Patty was fifteen when she left home for the first time to pay a visit to her Aunt Martha in London. Patty's home was in the country (for her father was a farmer), so she was very eager to see all the wonders of London. Her father drove her into the market-town very early on the morning of her departure, and as it was a very busy day with him, he was obliged to leave her in the coach office all by herself, as the London coach was not expected to start for half an hour. Patty kissed her father with tears in her eyes, and he blessed her; and telling her to be a good girl and "not learn silly town ways," he strode off, whip in hand, towards the market-place, leaving Patty alone with her possessions.

(2) They were not many—a leathern trunk that held all her wardrobe, a basket of flowers that hid a dozen of the largest and freshest eggs from her mother's poultry-yard, and last—to Patty's extreme annoyance—a doll that her mother had insisted on making and sending to little Betsy, Aunt Martha's youngest child. Patty herself had not long passed the age for loving dolls, and was, therefore, all the more sensitive on the subject; so when the coach came thundering into the yard, and she was called to take her place by a man who addressed her as "Little Missy," she was ready to shed tears of vexation. Patty had to remember her mother's words, to "take great care of the doll, as it had been a lot of trouble to make," otherwise she might have been tempted to leave it behind, or let it drop out of the coach window.

(3) Windsor was passed after a time, then Staines, and as the twilight came on the coach was going at a good pace, with the last rays of sunset to the left behind it, and the dark stretch of Hounslow Heath, with its dismal gallows, in front. Suddenly the coach stopped, and was surrounded by three men on horseback, armed with pistols, their faces hidden behind black crape masks. The ladies screamed, the men turned pale and trembled, the guard made a faint show of resistance, but was at once overpowered; the driver looked on with apparent indifference while the coach was ransacked.

(4) Patty had nothing worth taking—neither watch, jewels, nor money; but when asked by one of the men what she had, she held out the doll, almost hoping that he might take it, but he only laughed loudly. In a short time the coach was allowed to proceed on its way, Patty being the only traveler who had not been robbed.

(5) Very glad was Patty to see her uncle's kind face when the coach stopped in London at the end of its journey, and great was the excitement when it became known that they had been attacked by the way. When Patty told the story of the highwaymen to her aunt, and how she had offered them her doll, Aunt Martha gave a cry of horror.

(6) "Dear child; you were nearer the truth than you knew!" she said; and taking a pair of scissors, she cut the stitches that held together the rag body of the doll, and there fell out some golden coins on the table, that the farmer had sent to his sister to pay for his Patty while she was in London.

(7) Patty enjoyed her visit to London, and came home again quite safely, as did the doll, which Patty asked if she might keep in remembrance of that eventful journey.

When you're asked to determine the theme of a story, think about the main character. How does the main character's attitude or outlook change? That change is a clue about the theme.

Exercises

1. Why is Patty so resentful about having to carry the doll with her to London?

   A. She is much too old to play with dolls.
   B. She has just passed the age of playing with dolls.
   C. The doll is homemade and not something Patty wants to take to London.
   D. Patty wants the people on the coach to think she is much older than she is.

   RL.5.1

2. Which scene from the text best supports the story's theme of hidden value?

   A. Patty is tempted to drop the doll out the window of the coach.
   B. Patty asks if she can keep the doll when she returns home from London.
   C. The robbers laugh at Patty when she offers them the doll.
   D. Patty had to carry a basket of eggs and flowers, as well as the doll and her suitcase when she traveled to London.

   RL.5.2

3. Which statement accurately contrasts Patty's attitudes in paragraphs 2 and 7?

   A. In paragraph 2, Patty thought the doll was worthless, but in paragraph 7 she realized it hid great value.
   B. In paragraph 2, Patty thought the doll was a childish toy, but in paragraph 7 she realized it was appropriate for a girl her age.
   C. In paragraph 2, Patty was embarrassed to carry the doll, but in paragraph 7 she was proud of it.
   D. In paragraph 2, Patty resented having to carry the doll, but in paragraph 7 she wanted it as a souvenir of her adventure.

   RL.5.3

4. Which are synonyms for "vexation" as it is used in paragraph 2?

   A. Interest and embarrassment
   B. Frustration and annoyance
   C. Confusion and anger
   D. Fear and weariness

   RL.5.4

5. What important event connects the scenes in paragraphs 4 and 5?

   A. Patty was relieved to see her uncle.
   B. Patty finally arrived in London
   C. Patty offered the doll to the robbers.
   D. Patty decided she wanted to keep the doll after all.

   RL.5.5

6. How might the story have been different if told from the point of view of Patty?

   A. Paragraph 2 would not have focused on Patty's reaction to taking the doll.
   B. Paragraph 3 would have focused on Patty's reaction to the robbery.
   C. Paragraph 4 would have given a more thorough description of what Patty had with her.
   D. Paragraph 5 would have included information about what Patty did while she was in London.

   RL.5.6

Black History Month *By Jill Mountain*

What is Black History?

(1) Black history is the study of the experience of African Americans. The dates of African American history extend back to the earliest transport of African slaves, in 1619. Early African American history is sparsely documented. African American history often focuses on the achievements of civil rights pioneers and leaders who fought to overcome slavery. It covers the many decades of discrimination that followed the abolition of slavery. In the modern, Post-Civil Rights era, new African-American leaders and movements have emerged. There are new topics to study as more people of color make inroads into American politics, science, and the arts.

How Black History Month Began

(2) Carter G. Woodson, an African American historian, founded an academic organization to study how African Americans contributed to civilization. His organization was called The Association for the Study of Negro Life and History. In February of 1925, as part of the founding of the organization, Woodson organized the first Negro History Week. He chose February because it was the birth month of both Abraham Lincoln and Frederick Douglass. Abraham Lincoln was the American President who signed the Emancipation Proclamation. Frederick Douglass was an escaped slave who became an important social reformer and abolitionist.

Growing Awareness of Black History

(3) By the 1950s Negro History Week was well established around the country. Mayors of many cities made formal announcements each year to celebrate black history. Teachers in both black and white schools asked for materials to teach students about black leaders and events. In fact, by 1929, all but two State Departments of Education had provided schools with official literature about black history for use in classrooms. The "Black Awakening" of the 1960s led to even greater interest in the history of African Americans. Northern, urban blacks became empowered to pursue interests related to their unique cultural experiences. More and more African Americans attended college. University faculties used the month as an opportunity to highlight seldom-studied events in American history. They wanted to help black students better understand the important role of African Americans in the development of the United States. Predominately black churches publicized the week by encouraging congregations to set aside time to learn about their ancestors and communities. The event grew every year because of the efforts of many different organizations.

A Week Extended to a Month

(4) In 1976 President Gerald Ford said it was important that America "seize the opportunity to honor the too-often neglected accomplishments of black Americans..." Motivated by the bicentennial, America's 200th birthday, Ford proclaimed February would be Black History Month. Every year the president proclaims February as Black History Month.

TIP of the **DAY**

Cause and effect questions ask you to look at how one event affects or leads to another. To answer these questions, first find the cause in the text, then read to see how the author connects that cause to other events.

Exercises

1. Which statement from paragraph one supports the idea that black history is a field that is continually expanding?

   A. The dates of African American history extend back to the earliest transport of African slaves, in 1619.
   B. African American history often focuses on the achievements of civil rights pioneers and leaders who fought to overcome slavery.
   C. It covers the many decades of discrimination that followed the abolition of slavery.
   D. There are new topics to study as more people of color make inroads into American politics, science, and the arts.

   RL.5.1

2. What is the main idea of paragraph 4?

   A. President Ford is responsible for the observance of Black History Month
   B. President Ford made Black History Month an official observance in the United States.
   C. President Ford determined that Black History should be observed as part of the United States' 200th birthday.
   D. President Ford was encouraged by several leaders to begin observing Black History Month.

   RI.5.2

3. How did the Black Awakening affect interest in Black History Month?

   A. It created a need for more opportunities for young people to learn about black history.
   B. It led to more African Americans attending college and more directed research into black history.
   C. It created interest among black leaders who began to support Black History Month.
   D. It drew the attention of church leaders, who encouraged church members to learn about black history.

   RI.5.3

4. What is the most likely definition of the word "predominately" as it is used in this sentence, "Predominately black churches publicized the week by encouraging congregations to set aside time to learn about their ancestors and communities."

   A. Powerful
   B. Mostly
   C. Governmental
   D. Random

   RI.5.4

5. Which best describes how this passage is organized?

   A. It is organized using cause and effect, showing how events or incidents led to developments related to Black History Month.
   B. It is organized using problem and solution, showing how different leaders identified problems related to the African American community and sought to solve them by establishing Black History Month.
   C. It is organized chronologically, describing different people and events, in time order, that led to establishing Black History Month.
   D. It is organized in a series of comparisons, comparing important events in American History to the related events in Black History.

   RI.5.5

6. According to paragraph 2, February was chosen for Black History Month because...

   A. It is the birth month of two important Civil Rights figures.
   B. Woodson believed Lincoln was an important figure in black history.
   C. It is the same month that Lincoln signed the Emancipation Proclamation.
   D. It is a month closely associated with social reform and the abolition movement.

   RI.5.8

Excerpt from **The Secret Garden** *by Frances Hodgson Burnett*

(http://www.gutenberg.org/files/113/113-h/113-h.htm)

(1)   The sun shone down for nearly a week on the secret garden. The Secret Garden was what Mary called it when she was thinking of it. She liked the name, and she liked still more the feeling that when its beautiful old walls shut her in no one knew where she was. It seemed almost like being shut out of the world in some fairy place. The few books she had read and liked had been fairy-story books, and she had read of secret gardens in some of the stories. Sometimes people went to sleep in them for a hundred years, which she had thought must be rather stupid. She had no intention of going to sleep, and, in fact, she was becoming wider awake every day which passed.

(2)   She was beginning to like to be out of doors; she no longer hated the wind, but enjoyed it. She could run faster, and longer, and she could skip up to a hundred. The bulbs in the secret garden must have been much astonished. Such nice clear places were made round them that they had all the breathing space they wanted, and really, if Mistress Mary had known it, they began to cheer up under the dark earth and work tremendously. The sun could get at them and warm them, and when the rain came down it could reach them at once, so they began to feel very much alive.

(3)   Mary was an odd, determined little person, and now she had something interesting to be determined about, she was very much absorbed, indeed. She worked and dug and pulled up weeds steadily, only becoming more pleased with her work every hour instead of tiring of it. It seemed to her like a fascinating sort of play. She found many more of the sprouting pale green points than she had ever hoped to find. They seemed to be starting up everywhere and each day she was sure she found tiny new ones, some so tiny that they barely peeped above the earth.

(4)   There were so many that she remembered what Martha had said about the "snowdrops by the thousands," and about bulbs spreading and making new ones. These had been left to themselves for ten years and perhaps they had spread, like the snowdrops, into thousands. She wondered how long it would be before they showed that they were flowers. Sometimes she stopped digging to look at the garden and try to imagine what it would be like when it was covered with thousands of lovely things in bloom. During that week of sunshine, she became more intimate with Ben Weatherstaff. She surprised him several times by seeming to start up beside him as if she sprang out of the earth. The truth was that she was afraid that he would pick up his tools and go away if he saw her coming, so she always walked toward him as silently as possible. But, in fact, he did not object to her as strongly as he had at first. Perhaps he was secretly rather flattered by her evident desire for his elderly company. Then, also, she was more civil than she had been. He did not know that when she first saw him she spoke to him as she would have spoken to a native, and had not known that a cross, sturdy old Yorkshire man was not accustomed to salaam to his masters, and be merely commanded by them to do things.

Characters are transformed or changed by specific experiences. When you answer a question about a character changing, look for evidence to show that something in the character's life has changed.

Exercises

1. Describe the area the narrator refers to as the "secret garden?" Use details from the text.

RL.5.1

2. How does Mary's changing relationship with Weatherstaff support the theme of the text, the difficulty of adjusting to change?

RL.5.2

Exercises

3. How does Mary change because of the time she spends in the garden?

A. She grows stronger and healthier.
B. She becomes more patient with other people.
C. She begins to understand fairytales and stories she's read in the past.
D. She becomes more comfortable spending time alone.

RL.5.3

5. What important detail does the author introduce at the beginning of the passage to explain the events described in the story?

A. Mary was interested in fairy stories.
B. Mary had not read many books
C. The weather was sunny for an entire week.
D. Mary thought sleeping in a garden was stupid.

RL.5.5

4. What does the word "absorbed" mean as it is used in this sentence: "Mary was an odd, determined little person, and now she had something interesting to be determined about, she was very much absorbed, indeed."

A. Cleaned up
B. Interested
C. Taught
D. Paid for her work

RL.5.4

6. In which of the following excerpts does the narrator reveal Mary's thoughts or feelings?

A. She liked the name, and she liked still more the feeling that when its beautiful old walls shut her in no one knew where she was.
B. Mary was an odd, determined little person, and now she had something interesting to be determined about, she was very much absorbed, indeed.
C. She surprised him several times by seeming to start up beside him as if she sprang out of the earth.
D. Perhaps he was secretly rather flattered by her evident desire for his elderly company.

RL.5.6

WEEK 12

VIDEO
EXPLANATIONS

ARGOPREP.COM

Popular Entertainment in the 1920s From U.S. History

Download for free at http://cnx.org/contents/a7ba2fb8-8925-4987-b182-5f4429d48daa@3.32.

(1)   In the 1920s, prosperity manifested itself in many forms, most notably in advancements in entertainment and technology that led to new patterns of leisure and consumption. Movies and sports became increasingly popular and buying on credit or "carrying" the debt allowed for the sale of more consumer goods and put automobiles within reach of average Americans. Advertising became a central institution in this new consumer economy, and commercial radio and magazines turned athletes and actors into national icons.

(2)   The increased prosperity of the 1920s gave many Americans more disposable income to spend on entertainment. As the popularity of "moving pictures" grew in the early part of the decade, "movie palaces," capable of seating thousands, sprang up in major cities. A ticket for a double feature and a live show cost twenty-five cents; for a quarter, Americans could escape from their problems and lose themselves in another era or world. People of all ages attended the movies with far more regularity than today, often going more than once per week. By the end of the decade, weekly movie attendance swelled to ninety million people.

(3)   The silent movies of the early 1920s gave rise to the first generation of movie stars. Rudolph Valentino, the handsome man with the mysterious eyes, and Clara Bow, the "It Girl", filled the imagination of millions of American moviegoers. However, no star captured the attention of the American viewing public more than Charlie Chaplin. This sad-eyed tramp with a moustache, baggy pants, and a cane was the top box office attraction of his time.

(4)   In 1927, the world of the silent movie began to wane with the New York release of the first "talkie": The Jazz Singer. The plot of this film, which starred Al Jolson, told a distinctively American story of the 1920s. It follows the life of a Jewish man from his boyhood days of being groomed to be the religious leader at the local synagogue to his life as a famous and "Americanized" jazz singer. Both the story and the new sound technology used to present it were popular with audiences around the country. It quickly became a huge hit for Warner Brothers, one of the "big five" motion picture studios in Hollywood along with Twentieth Century Fox, RKO Pictures, Paramount Pictures, and Metro-Goldwyn-Mayer.

(5)   Southern California in the 1920s, however, had only recently become the center of the American film industry. Film production was originally based in and around New York, where Thomas Edison first debuted the kinetoscope in 1893. But in the 1910s, as major filmmakers like D. W. Griffith looked to escape the cost of Edison's patents on camera equipment, this began to change. When Griffith filmed In Old California (1910), the first movie ever shot in Hollywood, California, the small town north of Los Angeles was little more than a village. As moviemakers flocked to southern California, not least because of its favorable climate and predictable sunshine, Hollywood swelled with moviemaking activity. By the 1920s, the once-sleepy village was home to a majorly profitable innovative industry in the United States.

TIP of the DAY

Sequencing questions ask you to determine the order of events in a story. When answering a sequencing question, review all of the answer choices, and go back to the text to find dates, times, or other information that will help you determine the order of the events. Always confirm your answer with the text.

Exercises

1. What prompted filmmakers like D.W. Griffith to start producing movies in California, rather than New York?

A. They wanted to escape the cost of using Thomas Edison's equipment.
B. They wanted to start using the new "talking film" equipment.
C. They were interested in working with the first big movie stars, like Clara Bow and Charlie Chaplin.
D. They wanted to move to Hollywood while it was still a small town and an affordable place to start a business.

RI.5.3

4. Review the following sentence from paragraph 1. What word or phrase could be used to replace "national icons" in this sentence?

Advertising became a central institution in this new consumer economy, and commercial radio and magazines turned athletes and actors into national icons.

A. Movie stars
B. National heroes
C. Important leaders
D. Radio celebrities

RI.5.4

2. Why does the writer refer to the story of "The Jazz Singer" as an American story?

A. It is set in the United States.
B. It is about religion and music.
C. It is about a person's decision to follow his dream.
D. It is about a man who tries to hide the fact that he is an immigrant.

RI.5.1

5. Which of the following events occurred first, according to the article?

A. The Jazz Singer was released
B. Charlie Chaplin became a silent film star.
C. D.W. Griffith and others began making movies in California
D. Thomas Edison invented the kinetoscope.

RI.5.5

3. What is the main idea of paragraph 2?

A. Americans facing hardships enjoyed escaping to watch movies.
B. People had more time in the 1920s and could go to the movies more than once a week.
C. People had money to spend on entertainment in the 1920s, and spent it at the movies.
D. People attended movies because the theaters, or movie palaces, were large and could hold many people.

RI.5.2

6. The author of this text is writing about the changes in entertainment as a way to...

A. Explain one effect of Americans having more money in the 1920s.
B. Explain how people dealt with problems in the 1920s.
C. Explain how inventions in the 1920s and earlier affected average Americans.
D. Show how people began to define what it means to be an American.

RI.5.6

Learning to Read *By Frances Ellen Watkins Harper*

(https://www.poetryfoundation.org/poems-and-poets/poems/detail/52448)

Very soon the Yankee teachers
 Came down and set up school;
But, oh! how the Rebs did hate it,—
 It was agin' their rule.   (4)

Our masters always tried to hide
 Book learning from our eyes;
Knowledge did'nt agree with slavery—
 'Twould make us all too wise.   (8)

But some of us would try to steal
 A little from the book.
And put the words together,
 And learn by hook or crook.   (12)

I remember Uncle Caldwell,
 Who took pot liquor fat
And greased the pages of his book,
 And hid it in his hat.   (16)

And had his master ever seen
 The leaves upon his head,
He'd have thought them greasy papers,
 But nothing to be read.   (20)

And there was Mr. Turner's Ben,
 Who heard the children spell,
And picked the words right up by heart,
 And learned to read 'em well.   (24)

Well, the Northern folks kept sending
 The Yankee teachers down;
And they stood right up and helped us,
 Though Rebs did sneer and frown.   (28)

And I longed to read my Bible,
 For precious words it said;
But when I begun to learn it,
 Folks just shook their heads,   (32)

And said there is no use trying,
 Oh! Chloe, you're too late;
But as I was rising sixty,
 I had no time to wait.   (36)

So I got a pair of glasses,
 And straight to work I went,
And never stopped till I could read
 The hymns and Testament.   (40)

Then I got a little cabin
 A place to call my own—
And I felt independent
 As the queen upon her throne.   (44)

A stanza in a poem is like a paragraph in a story. As you read a poem, try to think about the main idea of each stanza before you go on to the next.

Exercises

1. In which stanza(s) does the poet give the reader a "hint" about the speaker's background?

A. Stanzas 1-2
B. Stanzas 3-4
C. Stanza 6
D. Stanza 8

RL.5.1

4. What does the poet mean in line 7, when she writes, "Knowledge did'nt agree with slavery.."

A. Many people did not know about slavery in the south.
B. Learning about slavery would make people angry.
C. Educated people would not allow themselves to remain slaves.
D. There was no time for slaves to acquire knowledge.

RL.5.4

2. What is a theme supported by this poem?

A. Education is best suited for the young.
B. Strangers cannot be trusted.
C. Education makes a person free.
D. To understand religion, a person must be educated.

RL.5.2

5. Why is the last stanza (lines 41-44) important to the poem?

A. It gives the reader information about the setting of the poem.
B. It shows how the speaker in the poem was able to overcome hardship.
C. It shows that as a result of learning to read, the speaker became independent.
D. It shows that the Yankee teachers cared about all of their students.

RL.5.5

3. According to the poem, what is the difference between "Yankees" and "Rebs?"

A. The Rebs knew more about slavery than the Yankees.
B. The Yankees wanted to educate African Americans, but the Rebs opposed it.
C. The Rebs were religious, but the Yankees were not.
D. The Yankees thought everyone could learn, but the Rebs believed only young people could be taught.

RL.5.3

6. What detail from the poem shows that the speaker was determined to learn to read?

A. She remembered people she'd known in the past who tried to learn to read.
B. She got a pair of glasses so she could see well enough to read.
C. She supported the Yankee teachers, even though it made the Rebs angry.
D. She escaped from slavery so that she could learn to read.

RL.5.6

Find detailed video explanations to each problem on:
ArgoPrep.com

Nerves From: Child's Health Primer

(https://www.gutenberg.org/files/25646/25646-h/25646-h.htm)

How do the muscles know when to move?

(1) You have all seen the telephone wires, by which messages are sent from one town to another, all over the country.

(2) You may be too young to understand how this is done, but you each have something inside of you, by which you are sending messages almost every minute while you are awake.

(3) We will try to learn a little about its wonderful way of working. In your head is your brain. It is the part of you which thinks. As you would be very badly off if you could not think, the brain is your most precious part, and you have a strong box made of bone to keep it in. We will call the brain the central telephone office. Little white cords, called nerves, connect the brain with the rest of the body. A large cord called the spinal cord, lies safely in a bony case made by the spine, and many nerves branch off from this.

(4) If you put your finger on a hot stove, in an instant a message goes on the nerve telegraph to the brain. It tells that wise thinking part that your finger will burn, if it stays on the stove. In another instant, the brain sends back a message to the muscles that move that finger, saying: "Contract quickly, bend the joint, and take that poor finger away so that it will not be burned."

(5) You can hardly believe that there was time for all this sending of messages; for as soon as you felt the hot stove, you pulled your finger away. But you really could not have pulled it away, unless the brain had sent word to the muscles to do it. Now, you know what we mean when we say, "As quick as thought." Surely nothing could be quicker. You see that the brain has a great deal of work to do, for it has to send so many orders.

(6) There are some muscles which are moving quietly and steadily all the time, though we take no notice of the motion. You do not have to think about breathing, and yet the muscles work all the time, moving your chest. If we had to think about it every time we breathed, we should have no time to think of any thing else.

(7) There is one part of the brain that takes care of such work for us. It sends the messages about breathing, and keeps the breathing muscles and many other muscles faithfully at work. It does all this without our needing to know or think about it at all. Do you begin to see that your body is a busy work-shop, where many kinds of work are being done all day and all night? Although we lie still and sleep in the night, the breathing must go on, and so must the work of those other organs that never stop until we die.

When a writer compares two things, he looks for similarities they share. When a writer contrasts two things, he looks for differences between them.

Exercises

1. What comparison does the author use to help the reader understand how nerves work?

   A. The author compares nerves to roads leading to the brain.
   B. The author compares nerves to telephone wires carrying messages.
   C. The author compares nerves to the automatic function of muscles.
   D. The author compares nerves to body functions that happen when people are asleep.

   RI.5.1

2. What is the main idea of paragraph 7?

   A. The body performs many functions completely automatically.
   B. The body is a workshop that creates new muscles and organs while we sleep.
   C. It is impossible to understand all the body functions that occur in a person's life.
   D. When organs stop functioning the body will die.

   RI.5.2

3. According to the passage, how are touching a hot stove and breathing alike?

   A. Both can be dangerous and require fast reaction times.
   B. Both are the result of actions from nerves in the spinal cord.
   C. Both involve automatic reactions that are not controlled by the conscious brain.
   D. Both involve a reaction to pain or being uncomfortable.

   RI.5.3

4. Review the following sentence from paragraph 7. What does the word "faithfully" mean as it is used in this sentence?

   "It sends the messages about breathing, and keeps the breathing muscles and many other muscles faithfully at work."

   A. Based in religious beliefs
   B. Truthful or honestly
   C. Reliable, something that can be counted on
   D. Determined, unwilling to give up

   RI.5.4

5. How does this passage use comparisons to explain complex ideas?

RI.5.5

6. What is the most likely reason the author wrote this passage in this tone and using these comparisons?

RI.5.6

WEEK 13

VIDEO
EXPLANATIONS

The Gift of the Magi *By O.Henry*

(https://www.auburn.edu/~vestmon/Gift_of_the_Magi.html)

(1) One dollar and eighty-seven cents. That was all. And sixty cents of it was in pennies. Pennies saved one and two at a time by bulldozing the grocer and the vegetable man and the butcher until one's cheeks burned with the silent imputation of parsimony that such close dealing implied. Three times Della counted it. One dollar and eighty- seven cents. And the next day would be Christmas.

(2) There was clearly nothing to do but flop down on the shabby little couch and howl. So Della did it. Which instigates the moral reflection that life is made up of sobs, sniffles, and smiles, with sniffles predominating.

(3) While the mistress of the home is gradually subsiding from the first stage to the second, take a look at the home. A furnished flat at $8 per week. It wasn't necessarily a home for beggars, but beggars would find themselves feeling at home there.

(4) In the vestibule below was a letter-box into which no letter would go, and an electric button from which no mortal finger could coax a ring. Also there was a card bearing the name "Mr. James Dillingham Young."

(5) The "Dillingham" had been flung to the breeze during a former period of prosperity when its possessor was being paid $30 per week. Now, when the income was shrunk to $20, though, they were thinking seriously of contracting to a modest and unassuming D. But whenever Mr. James Dillingham Young came home and reached his flat above he was called "Jim" and greatly hugged by Mrs. James Dillingham Young, already introduced to you as Della. Which is all very good.

(6) Della finished her cry and attended to her cheeks with the powder rag. She stood by the window and looked out dully at a gray cat walking a gray fence in a gray backyard. Tomorrow would be Christmas Day, and she had only $1.87 with which to buy Jim a present. She had been saving every penny she could for months, with this result. Twenty dollars a week doesn't go far. Expenses had been greater than she had calculated. They always are. Only $1.87 to buy a present for Jim. Her Jim. Many a happy hour she had spent planning for something nice for him. Something fine and rare and sterling-- something just a little bit near to being worthy of the honor of being owned by Jim.

(7) There was a pier-glass between the windows of the room. Perhaps you have seen a pier-glass in an $8 flat. A very thin and very agile person may, by observing his reflection in a rapid sequence of longitudinal strips, obtain a fairly accurate conception of his looks. Della, being slender, had mastered the art.

(8) Suddenly she whirled from the window and stood before the glass. her eyes were shining brilliantly, but her face had lost its color within twenty seconds. Rapidly she pulled down her hair and let it fall to its full length.

(9) Now, there were two possessions of the James Dillingham Youngs in which they both took a mighty pride. One was Jim's gold watch that had been his father's and his grandfather's. The other was Della's

If a story seems complicated, read it in short sections, and stop to summarizing it in your mind before moving on to the next section. Try reading one or two paragraphs at a time.

hair. Had the queen of Sheba lived in the flat across the airshaft, Della would have let her hair hang out the window some day to dry just to depreciate Her Majesty's jewels and gifts. Had King Solomon been the janitor, with all his treasures piled up in the basement, Jim would have pulled out his watch every time he passed, just to see him pluck at his beard from envy.

Exercises

1. Which sentence below best describes how Della feels about her husband?

A. Della resents her husband and thinks he's responsible for their poverty.
B. Della feels sorry for her husband because he is not as successful as he once was.
C. Della loves her husband very much and believes he deserves the best gift money can buy.
D. Della loves her husband but feels he asks too much of her.

RL.5.1

2. What problem does Della solve at the end of this excerpt?

A. How to fix up their apartment so it seems less poor and miserable.
B. How to find money to buy Jim a gift.
C. How to tell Jim she cannot afford to buy him a gift.
D. How to deal with her neighbors.

RL.5.2

3. Why does Della flop down and cry in paragraph 2?

A. Because she hates living in their shabby apartment.
B. Because she knows they don't have enough money to pay for their expenses.
C. Because her husband's salary has been decreased.
D. Because she thinks her goal of buying Jim a nice gift is hopeless.

RL.5.3

4. Read the following sentence from paragraph 1. What does it mean to "bulldoze" as the phrase is used in this sentence?

"Pennies saved one and two at a time by bulldozing the grocer and the vegetable man and the butcher..."

A. Pushing over
B. Stealing from
C. Negotiating prices
D. Refusing to buy products from

RL.5.4

5. What happens earlier in the story that leads to the problem described in this passage?

A. Jim and Della move to a cheaper apartment.
B. Jim decides to start using a different name.
C. Della has to give up her job.
D. Jim's pay is cut.

RL.5.5

6. What can the reader infer from paragraphs 8-9?

A. Della plans to move away to a place where her neighbors will be wealthy.
B. Della thinks her hair is valuable and can help her buy a gift for Jim.
C. Della thinks Jim should sell his pocket watch so they have more money for their home.
D. Della wishes she were wealthy like her neighbors.

RL.5.1

Chinese New Year *By Jill Mountain*

(1) Lunar New Year on the Chinese calendar is one of the most important festivals in Chinese culture. It is also called Spring Festival. Many westerners often refer to the holiday as Chinese New Year. The more accurate term is Lunar New Year. Many Asian countries, including Vietnam, Korea, and Taiwan celebrate the festival. It is not unique to China.

(2) The Chinese calendar is a lunisolar calendar. The dates are determined from both the earth moving around the sun and the phases of the moon. This way of marking time is different from the calendar used in the United States. The Western calendar used in the United States is called the Gregorian calendar. The Gregorian calendar is a tropical calendar. It determines dates only by the earth's rotation around the sun.

(3) The traditional Chinese calendar has twelve months. Chinese New Year's celebrations begin on the night before the first day of the new year. The festival lasts fifteen days. The dates of the festival change every year because of the phases of the moon. In 2015, it began on February 19. It was on February 8 in 2016. Each year the start date is different.

(4) The new year is a time to sweep away the hardships of the past year. People symbolically sweep away the past by cleaning their homes from top to bottom. They also buy new clothes. They have their hair cut. They prepare special foods that symbolize new beginnings. All the cleaning and preparations for the new year are finished before the start of the festival. Cleaning the house on the first day of the new year is considered bad luck.

(5) The festival is also a time to honor ancestors and gods. Families gather for large dinners on the night before the start of the festival. They share stories of their family history. They often exchange small gifts. They prepare and eat traditional family recipes. For many families, New Year's Eve is the largest family gathering of the year. In China young people often move away from their homes to study or work in large cities. They do not return to their hometowns very often. The fifteen days of the New Year's Festival is the biggest travel season in China. Railroads add additional routes to accommodate the many travelers. Travelers often buy train and bus tickets months in advance to travel during what is called the "Spring Rush." Even then, they experience long lines, delays, and nearly unbearable crowds.

(6) Those who celebrate Lunar New Year decorate their homes for the season, much like people in Western countries put up Christmas decorations in December. Red is a symbolic color in New Year decorations. Red is the color of good luck. It was once believed to ward off a monster named Nian, who, according to legend, came on the first day of the year to terrorize humans. The color gold is also popular in Lunar New Year decorations. Gold symbolizes wealth. Firecrackers are a fun and sometimes loud part of decorating for the new year. In rural areas, fire crackers are lit and set off. The loud noise is supposed to scare off evil spirits and bad luck. In more populated areas decorative firecrackers are hung with other ornaments inside and outside of homes. They are not lit or set off. The firecrackers are printed with messages of good luck. The messages are called Spring Couplets, and offer wishes of good health, prosperity, and friendship.

  *Make connections between new information and what you already know. When a passage uses a term you're familiar with, ask yourself if there is new information you can add to your understanding.*

Exercises

1. Which paragraph compares Chinese and Western calendars?

A. 1
B. 2
C. 3
D. 4

RI.5.1

4. Read the following sentence from paragraph 5. Which is the best definition of "accommodate" as it is used in this sentence?

"Railroads add additional routes to accommodate the many travelers."

A. Perform services for
B. Provide space for
C. Offer room for an overnight stay, such as a guest room or hotel room
D. Go along with requests

RI.5.4

2. What is the main idea of paragraph 5?

A. Many Chinese young people move away from their home towns.
B. Chinese people spend time with their families during New Year's celebrations.
C. New Year's is the biggest travel time of the year in China for several reasons.
D. Chinese transportation systems are not prepared for the great number of people who travel during the New Year's festival.

RI.5.2

5. Who is the author's intended audience for this passage?

A. Chinese people who live in the United States and want to explain Lunar New Year to others.
B. People who are not Chinese but are interested in this festival.
C. People who are planning to visit China during the Lunar New Year Festival.
D. People who are considering moving to China and want to know about busy travel times.

RI.5.7

3. What is a similarity between the Chinese calendar and the Western calendar?

A. Both are based on the phases of the moon.
B. Both are based on the earth's rotation around the sun.
C. Both change the date of the New Year each year based on the earth's position.
D. Both have twelve months.

RI.5.3

6. What is NOT an example the author uses to elaborate on the point that the Lunar New Year is considered a "new beginning?"

A. People buy new clothes
B. Special foods are prepared
C. People share stories about their families
D. People clean their homes thoroughly

RI.5.8

Excerpt from **The Phoenix and the Carpet** *by E. Nesbit*

(http://www.gutenberg.org/files/836/836-h/836-h.htm)

(1)   The bird rose in its nest of fire, stretched its wings, and flew out into the room. It flew round and round, and round again, and where it passed the air was warm. Then it perched on the fender. The children looked at each other. Then Cyril put out a hand towards the bird. It put its head on one side and looked up at him, as you may have seen a parrot do when it is just going to speak, so that the children were hardly astonished at all when it said, 'Be careful; I am not nearly cool yet.'

(2)   They were not astonished, but they were very, very much interested.

(3)   They looked at the bird, and it was certainly worth looking at. Its feathers were like gold. It was about as large as a rooster, only its beak was not at all rooster-shaped. 'I believe I know what it is,' said Robert. 'I've seen a picture.'

(4)   He hurried away. A hasty dash and scramble among the papers on father's study table yielded, as the sum-books say, 'the desired result'. But when he came back into the room holding out a paper, and crying, 'I say, look here,' the others all said 'Hush!' and he hushed obediently and instantly, for the bird was speaking.

(5)   'Which of you,' it was saying, 'put the egg into the fire?'

(6)   'He did,' said three voices, and three fingers pointed at Robert.

(7)   The bird bowed; at least it was more like that than anything else.

(8)   'I am your grateful debtor,' it said with a high-bred air.

(9)   The children were all choking with wonder and curiosity—all except Robert. He held the paper in his hand, and he KNEW. He said so, he said—

(10)   'I know who you are.'

(11)   And he opened and displayed a printed paper, at the head of which was a little picture of a bird sitting in a nest of flames.

(12)   'You are the Phoenix,' said Robert, and the bird was quite pleased.

(13)   'My fame has lived then for two thousand years,' it said. 'Allow me to look at my portrait.' It looked at the page which Robert, kneeling down, spread out in the fender, and said—

(14)   'It's not a flattering likeness, and what are these characters?' it asked, pointing to the printed part.

(15)   'Oh, that's all dullish, it's not much about YOU, you know,' said Cyril, with unconscious politeness, 'but you're in lots of books.'

Sometimes making a drawing or diagram of what is happening in a story can help you understand the action. Are characters moving around? Plot them out on a small map.

(16) 'With portraits?' asked the Phoenix.

(17) 'Well, no,' said Cyril, 'in fact, I don't think I ever saw any portrait of you but that one, but I can read you something about yourself, if you like.'

(18) The Phoenix nodded, and Cyril went off and fetched Volume X of the old Encyclopedia, and on page 246 he found the following:—

(19) 'Phoenix—in ornithology, a fabulous bird of antiquity.'

(20) 'Antiquity is quite correct,' said the Phoenix, 'but fabulous—well, do I look it?'

(21) Every one shook its head, Cyril went on—

(22) 'The ancients speak of this bird as single, or the only one of its kind.'

(23) 'That's right enough,' said the Phoenix.

(24) 'They describe it as about the size of an eagle.'

(25) 'Eagles are of different sizes,' said the Phoenix, 'it's not at all a good description.'

(26) All the children were kneeling on the hearthrug, to be as near the Phoenix as possible.

(27) 'You'll boil your brains,' it said. 'Look out, I'm nearly cool now,' and with a whirr of golden wings it fluttered from the fender to the table. It was so nearly cool that there was only a very faint smell of burning when it had settled itself on the table-cloth.

Exercises

1. Using evidence from the text, explain how the phoenix feels about being brought back.

_____

_____

_____

_____

_____

_____

_____

_____

_____

RL.5.1

2. How does this passage support the theme of "self-awareness" or "knowing yourself?"

RL.5.2

3. Which of the phoenix's statements give the children the impression they can trust him?

A. 'Be careful; I am not nearly cool yet.'
B. 'Which of you,' it was saying, 'put the egg into the fire?'
C. 'My fame has lived then for two thousand years,' it said.
D. 'Eagles are of different sizes,' said the Phoenix, 'it's not at all a good description.'

RL.5.3

5. How do paragraphs 19-25 contribute to the development of the passage?

A. Paragraphs 19-25 give the reader information about why the phoenix is visiting the children.
B. Paragraphs 19-25 provide information about the setting of the story.
C. Paragraphs 19-25 provide the reader with background information about the phoenix.
D. Paragraphs 19-25 provide the reader with important details about Robert's personality.

RL.5.5

4. Which statement has a meaning most similar to the phoenix's statement, "I am your grateful debtor," in paragraph 8?

A. Thank you.
B. I owe you for releasing me.
C. Now that I'm free, you must pay me.
D. Now that I'm free, I must find the people who trapped me.

RL.5.4

6. Review the image of the phoenix. What detail from the text is evident in this drawing?

A. The phoenix is a "bird of antiquity"
B. The phoenix is shown, in a book, sitting in a "nest of flames."
C. The phoenix is about the size of an eagle.
D. d.The phoenix has golden wings.

RL.5.7

WEEK 14

VIDEO
EXPLANATIONS

ARGOPREP.COM

From **Tom Swift and his Giant Telescope** *By Victor Appleton*

(http://www.gutenberg.org/files/21188/21188-h/21188-h.htm#CHAPTER_I)

(1)   Tom Swift appeared to be calm, although in reality he was about as excited over his latest invention as he ever had been about anything in his life.

(2)   "I'm sure it's going to work, Ned!" he said eagerly to his chum as they neared Tom's private laboratory. "With my new device I hope to learn more about the planets. I want to start soon—"

(3)   "Listen here!" broke in Ned Newton. "If you're thinking of going to Mars or the moon, just count me out! I've gone with you to many strange places and have never kicked. But this—"

(4)   "Hold on, young fellow!" interrupted the youthful inventor with an amused chuckle. "I've nothing like that in mind YET! All I want to do is show you my new 'space eye.'"

(5)   "Can't say as I like that word 'yet,'" Ned muttered darkly. "But I'll take a look at your new jigger if you'll promise not to shoot me through space in a rocket or cannon-ball!"

(6)   "Word of honor I won't," promised Tom, crossing his heart with mock solemnity. "Well, here we are."

(7)   The two boys had reached the laboratory, a small building at the rear of the spacious lawn surrounding Tom's father's home and close to the extensive work of the Swift Manufacturing Company at Shopton.

(8)   "Here goes!" said the young inventor.

(9)   He rolled back a small rug in the middle of the floor to expose a massive steel trap door. This he unlocked by twirling the dial of a complicated mechanism. Some years before Tom had constructed beneath his laboratory an impregnable chamber to safeguard his secret plans. He called it his Chest of Secrets, and guarded it well.

(10)   "Here it is," said Tom, joining his chum after a few minutes spent in the vault.

(11)   He was carrying a small wooden box which he placed on the desk and opened. If Ned, as he leaned over eagerly, expected to see anything astonishing he was disappointed. Resting on the velvet lining was simply a round disk of a greenish substance perhaps six inches in diameter. This was mounted in a gleaming metal ring from the edges of which there projected five electric binding posts.

(12)   "Funny kind of an eye," observed Ned. "You can't even see through it."

(13)   "You'll soon see through it, all right," retorted Tom, laying the disk on his desk and connecting four dry cells to the binding posts. He placed a small rheostat in the circuit so that the strength of the current might be regulated.

(14)   Slowly he moved the little handle over the graduated dial. A minute passed during which, so far as Ned could see, nothing happened. Without warning the green crystal suddenly glowed brightly for a fraction of a second, then could not be seen at all. The polished ring of metal in which it had been mounted alone remained.

(15)   "It's gone!" cried Ned in bewilderment. "I can see your desk top right through where it was!"

(16)   "No," smiled the inventor, "it's still there as you'll find if you try to poke your finger through the metal ring."

  *When a story has a lot of very specific details about an item that is important to the story, use those details to make a drawing. Sketch out the details described to improve your understanding.*

Exercises

1. Which detail from the story best helps the reader visualize Tom's invention?

A. "Funny kind of an eye," observed Ned. "You can't even see through it."
B. He was carrying a small wooden box which he placed on the desk and opened.
C. Resting on the velvet lining was simply a round disk of a greenish substance perhaps six inches in diameter.
D. Slowly he moved the little handle over the graduated dial.

RL.5.1

4. In paragraph 6, what does it mean that Tom is crossing his heart "with mock solemnity."

A. He is making fun of Ned.
B. He is lying when he promises they are not going into space.
C. He is pretending to be very serious.
D. He is hiding a secret from Ned, which he does not plan to reveal.

RL.5.4

2. What adjective best describes Ned's attitude about Tom's new invention, in paragraphs 1-6?

A. Confused
B. Nervous
C. Disbelieving
D. Frustrated

RL.5.2

5. What is Ned's main problem in paragraphs 1-5?

A. He doesn't want to go with Tom to his laboratory.
B. He doesn't understand the invention Tom wants to show him.
C. He's afraid Tom is planning something dangerous for them to do.
D. He is nervous that Tom is lying to him about his plans.

RL.5.5

3. What is Tom's reaction to Ned's "bewilderment" in paragraph 16?

A. Ned's confusion pleases Tom, as he then has an opportunity to tell him more about the invention.
B. Ned's confusion amuses Tom because he thinks it is funny that Ned doesn't understand basic science.
C. Tom is annoyed by Ned's confusion, since he's tried to explain the invention and Ned doesn't understand.
D. Tom is understanding of Ned's confusion, since he realizes that Ned is not as intelligent as he is.

RL.5.3

6. In paragraphs 11-16 it is clear that the narrator...

A. Is telling the story from Ned's point of view.
B. Assumes the reader is not familiar with scientific terms.
C. Is writing from the point of view of someone who understands Tom's invention.
D. Is a first-person narrator.

RL.5.6

Find detailed video explanations to each problem on:
ArgoPrep.com

Thomas Edison Wikipedia

(https://simple.wikipedia.org/wiki/Thomas_Edison, http://creativecommons.org/licenses/by-sa/3.0/)

(1)   Thomas Alva Edison was born in Milan, Ohio. When Edison was seven years old, he moved with his family to Port Huron, Michigan. Edison started school late because of an illness. Three months later, Edison was removed from school, because he could not pay attention to his teacher. His mother, who was a teacher in Canada, taught Edison at home. Edison's mother helped him become motivated for learning, and he was a good student to her.

(2)   When Edison was twelve years old, he contracted scarlet fever. The effects of the fever, as well as getting picked up by the ears by a train conductor, caused Edison to become completely deaf in his left ear, and 80 percent deaf in the other. He learned Morse code of the telegraph, and began a job as a "brass pounder" (telegraph operator). At age sixteen, Edison invented his first invention, which was called an "automatic repeater." It sent telegraph signals between unmanned stations, allowing almost anyone to translate code easily and precisely at one's own speed and convenience.

(3)   In 1868, Edison moved East and began to work for the Western Union Company in Boston, Massachusetts as a telegraph operator. He worked twelve hours a day, six days a week, and continued to "moonlight" on his own projects. Within six months, he had applied for and received his first patent for an electric vote recorder. It made the voting process faster but he could not find buyers. Then, Edison moved to New York and began to work for a company fixing their machines. At night, he continued to work on his projects and began to have some success selling his inventions.

(4)   In 1876 Edison used the money from his inventions to start his own laboratory in New Jersey. In 1877~78, he invented there the carbon microphone, which made the sound for Alexander Graham Bell's new telephone invention louder. In 1877, Edison invented the phonograph, the first machine that could record and play sound. The phonograph made him internationally famous. In 1879, Edison made a light bulb that lasted longer than those already available. Another invention, the electric power distribution network, made it possible to transmit electricity to buildings.

(5)   He married Mary Stilwell in 1871. He had three children in that marriage: Marion Estelle Edison (also called Dot), Thomas Alva Edison, Jr. (also called Dash) and William Leslie Edison. Mary Stilwell died in 1884. In 1885, Thomas Edison bought some land in Florida and built a house, where he would spend many winter months. In 1886, when he was thirty-nine, Edison married his second wife, Mina Miller, who was 19. He had 3 children in that marriage: Madeleine Edison, Charles Edison (who took over the company when his father died and was later elected Governor of New Jersey), and Theodore Miller Edison.

List of Thomas Edison's Inventions:

Year	Invention
1868	Electrical vote recorder
1869	Universal stock ticker
1872	Automatic telegraph system
	Paraffin paper (wax paper)
	Carbon rheostat (an instrument to control electrical current)
1876	Electric pen for mimeograph machines (early copiers)
1877	Telephone transmitter
	Phonograph (record player)
1891	Motion picture camera
1900	Nickel-iron-alkaline storage battery

TIP of the DAY

Charts provide a lot of information. After reviewing a chart, summarize the key information in your own words. Doing so will help you recall the main data points.

Exercises

1. Which of the following did Edison invent before he had his own laboratory?

   A. Wax paper
   B. Movie camera
   C. Record player
   D. Battery

RI.5.7

2. Thomas Edison died in 1931. In which paragraph should the writer include this information?

   A. 2
   B. 3
   C. 4
   D. 5

RI.5.7

3. Which of the following was a cause of Edison's hearing loss?

   A. Working as a "brass pounder"
   B. Lack of medical treatment
   C. Being removed from school
   D. Being injured by a train conductor

RI.5.5

4. What problem likely led to Edison inventing the "automatic repeater" for telegraph systems?

   A. Too few people knew the code necessary to send messages via telegraphs.
   B. Telegraph messages were transmitted too fast for many operators to decode.
   C. There were not telegraph offices in all communities.
   D. Telegraph messages were not always clearly transmitted.

RI.5.3

5. What is the main idea of paragraph 4?

   A. The phonograph, one of Edison's most famous inventions, enabled users to record and replay sound.
   B. Edison was able to improve upon existing designs of many products, including the lightbulb.
   C. Edison made some of his most famous inventions, including the phonograph and a microphone for telephones, after he started his own lab and became a full-time inventor.
   D. Edison worked closely with Alexander Graham Bell on many of his inventions.

RI.5.2

6. What inference can the reader make based on information in paragraph 5?

   A. Edison's first wife was opposed to moving to Florida.
   B. Edison's youngest three children grew up in Florida.
   C. Edison was financially successful as an inventor by 1885.
   D. Edison did not know his second wife very well when he married her in 1886.

RI.5.1

 Find detailed video explanations to each problem on:
ArgoPrep.com

You Are Old, Father William *By Lewis Carroll*

(http://storyit.com/Classics/JustPoems/youareold.htm)

"You are old, Father William," the young man said,   (1)
"And your hair has become very white;
 And yet you incessantly stand on your head-
 Do you think, at your age age, it is right?"

"In my youth," Father William replied to his son,   (5)
"I feared it might injure the brain;
 But, now that I'm perfectly sure I have none,
 Why, I do it again and again."

"You are old," said the youth, "as I mentioned before,
 And have grown most uncommonly fat;   (10)
 Yet you turned a back somersault in at the door-
 Pray, what is the reason of that?"

"In my youth," said the sage, as he shook his grey locks,
"I kept all my limbs very supple
 By the use of this ointment-one shilling the box-   (15)
 Allow me to sell you a couple?"

"You are old," said the youth, "and your jaws are too weak
 For anything tougher than suet;
 Yet you finished the goose, with the bones and the back-
 Pray, how did you manage to do it?"   (20)

"In my youth," said his father, "I took to the law,
 And argued each case with my wife;
 And the muscular strength, which it gave to my jaw,
 Has lasted the rest of my life."

"You are old," said the youth, "one would hardly suppose   (25)
 That your eye was steady as ever;
 Yet, you balanced an eel on the end of your nose-
 What made you so awfully clever?"

"I have answered three questions, and that is enough,"
 Said his father. "Don't give yourself airs!   (30)
 Do you think I can listen all day to such stuff?
 Be off, or I'll kick you downstairs!"

  *Always identify the "speaker" in a poem and determine if the speaker and the subject (who or what the poem is about) are the same.*

Exercises

1. Why do you think the poet wrote this poem?

RL.5.1

2. How does William feel about all the questions being asked of him?

RL.5.3

Exercises

3. Which statement best expresses the theme of this poem?

A. Young people should be more respectful to their elders.
B. It is never a good idea to assume older people are weak or slow.
C. The most clever people are always the oldest.
D. Sons can learn valuable lessons from their fathers if they take the time to listen.

RL.5.2

4. What lesson does this poem teach about human behavior?

A. Young people can learn a lot from their elders.
B. Young people can be annoying to their parents.
C. Older people should not be underestimated.
D. Older people are often rude and uncooperative.

RL.5.2

5. How is Father William feeling in the last stanza (lines 29-32)?

A. Impatient
B. Proud
C. Embarrassed
D. Tired

RL.5.1

6. What line or lines from the last stanza support your answer to question 5? Explain your answer.

RL.5.1

WEEK 15

VIDEO
EXPLANATIONS

ARGOPREP.COM

Excerpt from **Journey to the Center of the Earth** by *Jules Verne*

(http://www.gutenberg.org/files/18857/18857-h/18857-h.htm#CHAPTER_1)

A boy called Axel has accompanied his uncle, a German scientist, on an exploration into the crater of a volcano. Axel's uncle is trying to find a route to the center of the earth, and the group has been underground for many weeks. In this passage Axel realizes that he has become separated from his uncle.

(1)   To describe my despair would be impossible. No words could tell it. I was buried alive, with the prospect before me of dying of hunger and thirst. Mechanically I swept the ground with my hands. How dry and hard the rock seemed to me! But how had I left the course of the stream? For it was a terrible fact that it no longer ran at my side. Then I understood the reason of that fearful, silence, when for the last time I listened to hear if any sound from my companions could reach my ears. At the moment when I left the right road, I had not noticed the absence of the stream. It is evident that at that moment a deviation had presented itself before me, whilst the Hansbach [the stream], following the caprice of another incline, had gone with my companions away into unknown depths. How was I to return?

(2)   There was not a trace of their footsteps or of my own, for the foot left no mark upon the granite floor. I racked my brain for a solution of this impracticable problem. One word described my position. Lost! Lost at an immeasurable depth! Thirty leagues of rock seemed to weigh upon my shoulders with a dreadful pressure. I felt crushed. I tried to carry back my ideas to things on the surface of the earth.

(3)   There they were before me, but how unreal. Under the influence of a terrible hallucination I saw all the incidents of our journey pass before me like the scenes of a panorama. The ship and its inmates, Iceland, M. Fridriksson, and the great summit of Mount Sneffels! I said to myself that, if in my position I retained the most faint and shadowy outline of a hope, it would be a sure sign of approaching delirium. It were better to give way wholly to despair!

(4)   In fact, did I but reason with calmness and philosophy, what human power was there in existence able to take me back to the surface of the earth, and ready, too, to split asunder, to rend in twain those huge and mighty vaults which stand above my head? Who could enable me to find my road—and regain my companions?

(5)   It was silly of me even to hope to ever find my uncle again!

(6)   "Oh, Uncle!" was my despairing cry.

(7)   This was the only word of reproach which came to my lips; for I thoroughly understood how deeply and sorrowfully the worthy Professor would regret my loss, and how in his turn he would patiently seek for me.

(8)   When I at last began to resign myself to the fact that no further aid was to be expected from man, and knowing that I was utterly powerless to do anything for my own salvation, I kneeled with earnest fervor and asked assistance from Heaven. The remembrance of my innocent childhood, the memory of my mother, known only in my infancy, came welling forth from my heart. I had recourse to prayer. And little as I had a right to be remembered by Him whom I had forgotten in the hour of prosperity, and whom I so tardily invoked, I prayed earnestly and sincerely.

  *Use context clues to determine synonyms for unfamiliar words as you read. Then, read over the passage again using your synonyms to make sure you've understood the most important points.*

Exercises

1. Which sentence best supports the idea that the narrator believes there is nothing he can do to save himself?

   A. ... knowing that I was utterly powerless to do anything for my own salvation, I kneeled with earnest fervor and asked assistance from Heaven.
   B. I thoroughly understood how deeply and sorrowfully the worthy Professor would regret my loss, and how in his turn he would patiently seek for me.
   C. I racked my brain for a solution of this impracticable problem
   D. I tried to carry back my ideas to things on the surface of the earth.

   RL.5.1

2. What does Axel consider his first mistake, which led to him being so terribly lost?

   A. He did not focus on trying to find the footprints of others from his group.
   B. He forgot important lessons he learned while he was on a ship on his way to this adventure.
   C. He lost sight of the Hansbach, a stream the rest of the group was following.
   D. He counted on his uncle to notice he was missing.

   RL.5.3

3. What important information is introduced in the italicized prologue to this passage?

   A. Characters and setting
   B. The main conflict of the novel.
   C. The resolution of the story.
   D. An explanation of who the narrator is.

   RL.5.5

4. What information is not included in this passage because of the narrator's point of view?

   A. The age and physical appearance of the narrator.
   B. The location of Axel's uncle and the rest of the party
   C. What Axels sees when he looks around
   D. How Axel feels about his situation

   RL.5.6

5. How does Axel try to solve his problem by the end of the passage?

   A. He decides to wait for his uncle to find him.
   B. He decides he will walk back the way he came and look for footprints.
   C. He decides he will try to remember what direction his uncle and the others intended to follow.
   D. He decides to pray and hope that God will save him.

   RL.5.5

6. What does the phrase "resign myself to the fact" mean as it is used in paragraph 8?

   A. Quit working toward a solution.
   B. Accept that something is true.
   C. Hope that someone will take charge of solving a problem.
   D. Realize that someone will soon be there to help.

   RL.5.4

Cotton Candy *By J. Mountain*

(1)   It is ironic that the first cotton candy machine was invented by a dentist! Cotton candy is made by spinning warmed sugar into long threads. Before the invention of a machine, it was made by hand. Sugar was warmed slowly over low heat, then twirled with glass wands into long strands. The strands were spun into bundles. It could take up to an hour to make a single one ounce bundle of cotton candy. Only the wealthiest people could afford it.

(2)   In 1897, William James Morrison, a dentist from Nashville, TN, invented a machine that could make cotton candy more quickly and economically. Morrison's machine heated the sugar and used forced air to push the sugar through a fine screen. The user spun a wooden stick around the screen to collect the strands of sugar. The machine could make twenty bundles of cotton candy in the time it took to make one using the old method.

(3)   The cotton candy machine was a novelty. It did not attract wide attention until Morrison brought it to the 1904 World's Fair in St. Louis, MO. He called his product "Fairy Floss" and sold it for 25 cents a box, which is equivalent to $7.00 today. The World's Fair brought visitors from all over the United States, and all over the world. It included many cultural and scientific exhibits, and was the birthplace of several foods that are now part of American culture. The ice cream cone and the hamburger were first introduced at the fair. William Morrison sold almost 70,000 boxes of cotton candy at the World's Fair and introduced the treat to a huge audience.

(4)   Later inventors, including another dentist from New Orleans, LA, Joseph Lascaux improved the design. Lascaux was the first to call the treat "cotton candy" and in 1921 he began selling the confection from his a shop in New Orleans. Lascaux's machine was state of the art until the 1970s, when an automatic cotton candy machine was developed so that the treat could be produced and packaged in factories, then shipped to carnivals for sale.

(5)   Interestingly, cotton candy is sold by color, rather than flavor, and is usually available in blue, which has a raspberry flavor, and pink, which has a vanilla flavor. Today "cotton candy flavor" is used to describe a sweet, sugary vanilla flavor used in cakes, frosting, and even ice cream. There are about 110 calories in each ounce of cotton candy, and a typical service size is about two ounces.

Pay attention when an author points out that a detail is "ironic" or "interesting." That usually is a clue that the information is important.

Exercises

1. Based on paragraph 1, the reader can conclude that ironic most likely means...

   A. Incorrect
   B. Unexpected
   C. A legend or rumor
   D. Ridiculous

RI.5.4

4. What is the main idea of paragraph 4?

   A. Joseph Lascaux made the first cotton candy.
   B. Joseph Lascaux invented a way to manufacture cotton candy in factories
   C. Joseph Lascaux's improved cotton candy machine was the best available until the 1970s.
   D. Joseph Lascaux was a dentist, like William James Morrison.

RI.5.2

2. What could be considered the biggest "turning point" in the history of cotton candy's popularity?

   A. Changing the name from "fairy floss" to "cotton candy."
   B. William James Morrison's invention
   C. The 1904 World's Fair
   D. Automating cotton candy production in factories.

RI.5.3

5. In what sentence does the author imply that it once cost a lot of money to pay someone to make cotton candy?

   A. Before the invention of a machine, it was made by hand.
   B. The strands were spun into bundles.
   C. It could take up to an hour to make a single one ounce bundle of cotton candy.
   D. The machine could make twenty bundles of cotton candy in the time it took to make one using the old method.

RI.5.1

3. How is the information in this passage organized?

   A. Chronologically, or in time order.
   B. By cause and effect, explaining how different inventions and developments changed cotton candy production.
   C. By problem and solution, explaining the different challenges faced in making cotton candy, and how they were overcome.
   D. As a process or procedure, explaining the steps in making cotton candy.

RI.5.5

6. Which fact is not supported by the text?

   A. William James Morrison introduced a product called cotton candy to the fair goers.
   B. The World's Fair brought several new foods to the world, including hamburgers and ice cream cones.
   C. Morrison replaced glass wands with wooden sticks with his invention.
   D. Factory produced cotton candy is likely made more quickly than Morrison or Lascaux's product.

RI.5.2

Happiness From: Psychology

(http://cnx.org/contents/Sr8Ev5Og@5.52:260-b1FK@5/The-Pursuit-of-Happiness)

Download for free at http://cnx.org/contents/4abf04bf-93a0-45c3-9cbc-2cefd46e68cc@5.52.

(1)   What really makes people happy? What factors contribute to sustained joy and contentment? Is it money, attractiveness, material possessions, a rewarding occupation, a satisfying relationship? Extensive research over the years has examined this question. One finding is that age is related to happiness: Life satisfaction usually increases the older people get, but there do not appear to be gender differences in happiness (Diener, Suh, Lucas, & Smith, 1999).

(2)   Family and other social relationships appear to be key factors correlated with happiness. Studies show that married people report being happier than those who are single, divorced, or widowed (Diener et al., 1999). Happy individuals also report that their marriages are fulfilling (Lyubomirsky, King, & Diener, 2005). In fact, some have suggested that satisfaction with marriage and family life is the strongest predictor of happiness (Myers, 2000). Happy people tend to have more friends, more high-quality social relationships, and stronger social support networks than less happy people (Lyubomirsky et al., 2005). Happy people also have a high frequency of contact with friends (Pinquart & Sörensen, 2000).

(3)   Can money buy happiness? In general, extensive research suggests that the answer is yes, but with several caveats. While a nation's per capita gross domestic product (GDP) is associated with happiness levels (Helliwell et al., 2013), changes in GDP (which is a less certain index of household income) bear little relationship to changes in happiness (Diener, Tay, & Oishi, 2013). On the whole, residents of affluent countries tend to be happier than residents of poor countries; within countries, wealthy individuals are happier than poor individuals, but the association is much weaker (Diener & Biswas-Diener, 2002). To the extent that it leads to increases in purchasing power, increases in income are associated with increases in happiness (Diener, Oishi, & Ryan, 2013). However, income within societies appears to correlate with happiness only up to a point. In a study of over 450,000 U.S. residents surveyed by the Gallup Organization, Kahneman and Deaton (2010) found that well-being rises with annual income, but only up to $75,000. The average increase in reported well-being for people with incomes greater than $75,000 was zero. As implausible as these findings might seem—after all, higher incomes would enable people to indulge in Hawaiian vacations, prime seats as sporting events, expensive automobiles, and expansive new homes— higher incomes may hurt people's ability to savor and enjoy the small pleasures of life (Kahneman, 2011). Indeed, researchers in one study found that participants exposed to subtle reminders of wealth and money spent less time savoring a chocolate candy bar and exhibited less enjoyment of this experience than did participants who were not reminded of wealth (Quoidbach, Dunn, Petrides, & Mikolajczak, 2010).

(4)   What about education and employment? Happy people, compared to those who are less happy, are more likely to graduate from college and secure more meaningful and engaging jobs. Once they obtain a job, they are also more likely to succeed (Lyubomirsky et al., 2005). While education shows a positive (but weak) correlation with happiness, intelligence is not appreciably related to happiness (Diener et al., 1999).

When a paragraph begins with a question, that means the author intends to answer the question. A great trick to make sure you've understood a passage is to answer all the questions the author asks.

Exercises

1. According to this passage, why doesn't more money always equal more happiness?

2. How did researchers prove the relationship between happiness and higher incomes?

3. According to the author, which of the following groups is likely the happiest?

A. People who make more than $75,000 a year.
B. Young people
C. Married people
D. People who are more intelligent than average.

RI.5.1

5. Review this sentence from paragraph five and choose the word that is the best synonym for affluent as it is used in the sentence:

"On the whole, residents of affluent countries tend to be happier than residents of poor countries;"

A. Happy
B. Educated
C. Technological
D. Wealthy

RI.5.4

4. What is the relationship between happiness and education?

A. Highly educated people are generally much happier than people who are not highly educated.
B. Happier people are more likely to complete their education and find better jobs.
C. Happy people are less likely to complete their educations and find better jobs because their happiness is not dependent on their incomes.
D. More intelligent people find it easier to complete their educations, and, are therefore much happier in high school and in college.

RI.5.3

6. What is the main idea of paragraph 2?

A. Happy people attract positive attention from others.
B. Happy people are more likely to be married than to be single.
C. A good way to find happiness is to spend time with a lot of people.
D. Happy people spend a lot of time with their friends.

RI.5.3

WEEK 16

VIDEO
EXPLANATIONS

ARGOPREP.COM

All about Peanut Butter

(1) The use of peanuts dates to the Aztecs and Incas, and peanut paste may have been used by the Aztecs as a toothache remedy in the first century of the Common Era (CE).

(2) Marcellus Gilmore Edson (1849 – 1940) of Montreal, Quebec (in Canada) was the first to patent peanut butter in 1884. Edson's cooled product had "a consistency like that of butter, lard, or ointment" according to his patent application which described a process of milling roasted peanuts until the peanuts reached "a fluid or semi-fluid state". He mixed sugar into the paste to harden its consistency.

(3) John Harvey Kellogg, known for his line of prepared breakfast cereals, was issued a patent for a "Process of Producing Alimentary Products" in 1898, and used peanuts, although he boiled the peanuts rather than roasting them. Kellogg served peanut butter to the patients at his Battle Creek Sanitarium.

(4) Early peanut-butter-making machines were developed by Joseph Lambert, who had worked at John Harvey Kellogg's Battle Creek Sanitarium, and Dr. Ambrose Straub who obtained a patent for a peanut-butter-making machine in 1903."In 1922, chemist Joseph Rosefield invented a process for making smooth peanut butter that kept the oil from separating by using partially hydrogenated oil"; Rosefield "...licensed his invention to the company that created Peter Pan peanut butter" in 1928 and in "...1932 he began producing his own peanut butter under the name Skippy.

(5) As the US National Peanut Board confirms, "Contrary to popular belief, George Washington Carver did not invent peanut butter." January 24 is National Peanut Butter Day in the United States.

Types

(6) The two main types of peanut butter are crunchy (or chunky) and smooth. In crunchy peanut butter, some coarsely-ground peanut fragments are included to give extra texture. The peanuts in smooth peanut butter are ground uniformly.

(7) In the US, food regulations require that any product labelled "peanut butter" must contain at least 90% peanuts; the remaining <10% usually consists of "...salt, a sweetener, and an emulsifier or hardened vegetable oil which prevents the peanut oil from separating". In the US, no product labelled as "peanut butter" can contain "artificial sweeteners, chemical preservatives, [or] natural or artificial coloring additives." Some brands of peanut butter are sold without emulsifiers that bind the peanut oils with the peanut paste, and so require stirring after separation. Most major brands of peanut butter add white sugar, but there are others that use dried cane syrup, agave syrup or coconut palm sugar.

Organic

(8) In 2012, organic peanut butter was available. Since the market for organic peanut butter is small, there is not enough demand to support manufacturers who produce only organic peanut butter. As a result, most organic peanut butter is produced in factories that also make non-organic peanut butter.

After reading a challenging paragraph with a lot of information, always stop and restate the main points to yourself before going on to the next paragraph.

Exercises

1. How was John Harvey Kellogg's peanut butter different from peanut butter we buy in stores today?

   A. Kellogg's peanut butter used less sugar.
   B. Kellogg's peanut butter was a liquid, rather than a paste.
   C. Kellogg's peanut was made from boiled peanuts.
   D. Kellogg's peanut butter was organic.

   RI.5.3

2. Which paragraph from the text helps the reader understand how peanut butter is made?

   A. Paragraph 2
   B. Paragraph 4
   C. Paragraph 6
   D. Paragraph 7

   RI.5.1

3. How did Joseph Rosefeld change peanut butter so that it became more like the product most modern people are familiar with?

   A. He developed a way to make it smooth or crunchy, so people could choose which type they liked best.
   B. He used roasted peanuts, which changed the taste of peanut butter.
   C. He developed a process to keep the peanut oil from separating from the peanut butter.
   D. He found a way to sweeten the peanut butter with sweeteners other than white sugar.

   RI.5.3

4. What does the phrase "contrary to popular belief" mean as it is used in paragraph 5?

   A. Even though most people know it is true
   B. This is a very popular idea.
   C. It is opposite of what many people think, but...
   D. A well-known fact that is believed by many people is that...

   RI.5.4

5. A product that was 50% peanut butter and 50% chocolate could be marketed as...

   A. Peanut butter
   B. Smooth sweetened peanut butter
   C. Half peanut butter
   D. Anything but peanut butter

   RI.5.7

6. How does the author support his claim that George Washington Carver did not invent peanut butter?

   A. He cites an expert source: the US National Peanut Board
   B. He refers to patents for peanut butter making machines and notes that they were issued before Carver was born
   C. He explains how peanut butter brands like Peter Pan and Skippy were brought to market.
   D. He explains different types of peanut butter.

   RI.5.8

Find detailed video explanations to each problem on: **ArgoPrep.com**

The Story of Fidgety Philip *by Heinrich Hoffman*

(http://storyit.com/Classics/JustPoems/fidgetphilip.htm)

"Let me see if Philip can
Be a little gentleman;
Let me see if he is able
To sit still for once at table:"
Thus Papa bade Phil behave; (5)
And Mamma looked very grave.

But fidgety Phil,
He won't sit still;
He wriggles,
And giggles, (10)
And then, I declare,
Swings backwards and forwards,
And tilts up his chair,
Just like any rocking-horse-
"Philip! I am getting cross!" (15)

See the naughty, restless child
Growing still more rude and wild,
Till his chair falls over quite.
Philip screams with all his might,
Catches at the cloth, but then (20)
That makes matters worse again.
Down upon the ground they fall,
Glasses, plates, knives, forks, and all.
How Mamma did fret and frown,
When she saw them tumbling down! (25)
And Papa made such a face!
Philip is in sad disgrace.

Where is Philip, where is he?
Fairly covered up you see!
Cloth and all are lying on him; (30)
He has pulled down all upon him.
What a terrible to-do!
Dishes, glasses, snapped in two!
Here a knife, and there a fork!

Philip, this is cruel work. (35)
Table all so bare, and ah!
Poor Papa, and poor Mamma
Look quite cross, and wonder how
They shall have their dinner now.

A narrative poem tells a story. There characters and a plot. Read the poem as though you were reading a story.

Exercises

1. What inference can the reader make from the first stanza of this poem?

   A. Philip has promised to behave himself.
   B. Philip usually behaves badly at the table.
   C. Philip's parents are having friends over for dinner.
   D. Philip does not like what is being served for dinner.

   RL.5.1

2. What does Philip do that leads to the big mess at the end of the poem?

   A. He giggles and wiggles.
   B. He screams louder and louder.
   C. He rocks back and forth in his chair.
   D. He throws the dishes onto the floor.

   RL.5.1

3. What is most likely the speaker's attitude about the events described in the poem?

   A. The speaker thinks Philip's behavior was funny.
   B. The speaker believes Philip's parents should not have let him sit at the table.
   C. The speaker thinks Philip is disgraceful.
   D. The speaker believes Philip fell over accidentally and should be forgiven.

   RI.5.6

4. What does the word "grave" mean as it is used in line 6 of the poem?

   A. Like death
   B. Cold
   C. Afraid
   D. Serious

   RL.5.4

5. How would the poem be different if the third stanza (lines 16-22) were left out?

   A. The reader would not know that Philip refused to listen to his parents.
   B. The reader would not know that all the plates from the table ended up on the floor.
   C. The reader would not know how Philip's father reacted when he made a mess.
   D. The reader would not know how the plates and knives and forks ended up on the floor.

   RL.5.5

6. What is the best synonym for "cross" as it is used in line 38 of the poem?

   A. Confused
   B. Sad
   C. Frightened
   D. Angry

   RL.5.4

From **The Little Princess** By Frances Hodgson Burnett

(http://www.feedbooks.com/books?category=FBJUV000000)

Sarah

(1)   Once on a dark winter's day, when the yellow fog hung so thick and heavy in the streets of London that the lamps were lighted and the shop windows blazed with gas as they do at night, an odd-looking little girl sat in a cab with her father, and was driven rather slowly through the big thoroughfares.

(2)   She sat with her feet tucked under her, and leaned against her father, who held her in his arm, as she stared out of the window at the passing people with a queer old-fashioned thoughtfulness in her big eyes.

(3)   She was such a little girl that one did not expect to see such a look on her small face. It would have been an old look for a child of twelve, and Sara Crewe was only seven. The fact was, however, that she was always dreaming and thinking odd things, and could not herself remember any time when she had not been thinking things about grown-up people and the world they belonged to. She felt as if she had lived a long, long time.

(4)   At this moment she was remembering the voyage she had just made from Bombay with her father, Captain Crewe. She was thinking of the big ship, of the lascars passing silently to and fro on it, of the children playing about on the hot deck, and of some young officers' wives who used to try to make her talk to them and laugh at the things she said.

(5)   Principally, she was thinking of what a strange thing it was that at one time one was in India in the blazing sun, and then in the middle of the ocean, and then driving in a strange vehicle through strange streets where the day was as dark as the night. She found this so puzzling that she moved closer to her father.

(6)   "Papa," she said in a low, mysterious little voice which was almost a whisper, "papa."

(7)   "What is it, darling?" Captain Crewe answered, holding her closer and looking down into her face. "What is Sara thinking of?"

(8)   "Is this the place?" Sara whispered, cuddling still closer to him. "Is it, papa?"

(9)   "Yes, little Sara, it is. We have reached it at last." And though she was only seven years old, she knew that he felt sad when he said it.

(10)   It seemed to her many years since he had begun to prepare her mind for "the place," as she always called it. Her mother had died when she was born, so she had never known or missed her. Her young, handsome, rich, petting father seemed to be the only relation she had in the world. They had always played together and been fond of each other. She knew, though, that they would have to be apart for a time, and for this reason, she was sometimes sad.

(11)   She only knew he was rich because she had heard people say so when they thought she was not listening, and she had also heard them say that when she grew up she would be rich, too. She did not know

As you read a story try to make predictions about what will happen next. Read to confirm your predictions, or if you did not predict correctly, look for information you might have missed.

all that being rich meant. She had always lived in a beautiful bungalow, and had been used to seeing many servants who made salaams to her and called her "Missee Sahib", and gave her her own way in everything. She had had toys and pets and an ayah who worshipped her, and she had gradually learned that people who were rich had these things. That, however, was all she knew about it.

Exercises

1. Why did Sara not know she was rich until she heard other people talk about it when they thought she wasn't listening? Use text evidence to support your answer.

_____

_____

_____

_____

_____

_____

_____

RL.5.1

2. What does Sara's papa feel "sad" when he confirms that they have reached "the place?"

_____

_____

_____

_____

_____

_____

_____

RL.5.1

3. How does the setting of the passage contribute to the overall mood or feeling?

A. The setting is welcoming, which leads the reader to feel that "the place" will be a good experience for Sara.
B. The setting is dynamic and exciting, always changing, which gives the reader the impression that the story is about to become very exciting.
C. The setting is cold and drab, which suggests that nothing exciting will happen in this part of the story.
D. The setting is cold, and it is dark even during the day, which suggests the characters cannot see clearly what will happen next.

RL.5.3

5. What can the reader infer about Sara from paragraphs 1-3?

A. She has spent most of her time with adults.
B. She has been away from her father for a long time.
C. She is very unhappy about moving from India to London.
D. She is excited about starting a new life in London

RL.5.1

4. Based on the context clues in paragraph 4, the reader can infer that a lascar is most likely...

A. A type of ship made for long distance travel
B. An area on the ocean where the sea is calm
C. A sailor or worker on a ship
D. A soldier

RL.5.4

6. From the narrator's description of Papa, the reader can infer that...

A. He is eager to show Sara around London.
B. He is sad that they had to leave India.
C. He is sad because he and Sara will be separated soon.
D. He is eager to return to India without Sara.

RL.5.1

WEEK 17

VIDEO
EXPLANATIONS

ARGOPREP.COM

Find detailed video explanations to each problem on:
ArgoPrep.com

Memory – From Psychology

(http://cnx.org/contents/Sr8Ev5Og@5.52:-RwqQWzt@6/How-Memory-Functions)
Download for free at http://cnx.org/contents/4abf04bf-93a0-45c3-9cbc-2cefd46e68cc@5.52.

(1) Memory is an information processing system; therefore, we often compare it to a computer. Memory is the set of processes used to encode, store, and retrieve information over different periods of time.

ENCODING

(2) We get information into our brains through a process called encoding, which is the input of information into the memory system. Once we receive sensory information from the environment, our brains label or code it. We organize the information with other similar information and connect new concepts to existing concepts. Encoding information occurs through automatic processing and effortful processing.

(3) If someone asks you what you ate for lunch today, more than likely you could recall this information quite easily. This is known as automatic processing, or the encoding of details like time, space, frequency, and the meaning of words. Automatic processing is usually done without any conscious awareness. Recalling the last time you studied for a test is another example of automatic processing. But what about the actual test material you studied? It probably required a lot of work and attention on your part in order to encode that information. This is known as effortful processing.

(4) There are three types of encoding. The encoding of words and their meaning is known as semantic encoding. It was first demonstrated by William Bousfield (1935) in an experiment in which he asked people to memorize words. The 60 words were actually divided into 4 categories of meaning, although the participants did not know this because the words were randomly presented. When they were asked to remember the words, they tended to recall them in categories, showing that they paid attention to the meanings of the words as they learned them.

(5) Visual encoding is the encoding of images, and acoustic encoding is the encoding of sounds, words in particular. To see how visual encoding works, read over this list of words: car, level, dog, truth, book, value. If you were asked later to recall the words from this list, which ones do you think you'd most likely remember? You would probably have an easier time recalling the words car, dog, and book, and a more difficult time recalling the words level, truth, and value. Why is this? Because you can recall images (mental pictures) more easily than words alone. When you read the words car, dog, and book you created images of these things in your mind. These are concrete, high-imagery words. On the other hand, abstract words like level, truth, and value are low-imagery words. High-imagery words are encoded both visually and semantically (Paivio, 1986), thus building a stronger memory.

(6) Now let's turn our attention to acoustic encoding. You are riding in your car and a song comes on the radio that you haven't heard in at least 2 years, but you sing along, recalling every word. In the United States, children often learn the alphabet through song, and they learn the number of days in each month through rhyme: "Thirty days hath September, / April, June, and November; / All the rest have thirty-one, / Save February, with twenty-eight days clear, / And twenty-nine each leap year." These

When reading a scientific text, focus on key vocabulary. Underline or highlight words that are new to you and determine their meaning with information from the text.

lessons are easy to remember because of acoustic encoding. We encode the sounds the words make. This is one of the reasons why much of what we teach young children is done through song, rhyme, and rhythm.

Exercises

1. What evidence does the author provide to show that acoustic encoding makes it easier to remember information?

   A. People often sing along with the radio.
   B. Young children are often taught through songs and rhymes.
   C. Some words are high-imagery, which makes them easier to remember.
   D. Some words are encoded visually, based on what we see.

   RI.5.6

4. From information in paragraph 6, the reader can conclude that "acoustic" refers to...

   A. What people see
   B. What people remember
   C. What people hear
   D. What people can picture in their minds.

   RI.5.4

2. According to the text, learning a list of vocabulary words and their exact definitions is an example of...

   A. Semantic encoding
   B. Acoustic encoding
   C. Visual encoding
   D. Automatic processing

   RI.5.1

5. What evidence does the writer use to prove his point that people remember words by remembering their meanings?

   A. The results of a study conducted in 1935
   B. Examples from everyday life, such as remembering what you had for lunch.
   C. Referring to how people study for tests.
   D. By contrasting mental pictures for concrete words and abstract words.

   RI.5.8

3. A kindergarten teacher shows her students pictures, including a dog, a ball, and an apple. Under each picture the word for the image is also shown. According to the text, students who use these cards to learn new words are using all but which of the following?

   A. Semantic encoding
   B. Visual encoding
   C. Automatic processing
   D. Effortful processing

   RI.5.9

6. What is the main idea of paragraph 1?

   A. Memory is information stored in the human brain.
   B. Memory is a set of processes that are similar to a computer's processes.
   C. Memories can last for long periods of time depending on how they are encoded and stored.
   D. There are different ways to retain information in our memories.

   RI.5.2

From **The Story Girl** *By L.M. Montgomery*

(http://www.gutenberg.org/files/5342/5342-h/5342-h.htm#link2HCH0009)

(1)   "I do like a road, because you can be always wondering what is at the end of it."

(2)   The Story Girl said that once upon a time. Felix and I, on the May morning when we left Toronto for Prince Edward Island, had not then heard her say it, and, indeed, were but barely aware of the existence of such a person as the Story Girl. We did not know her at all under that name. We knew only that a cousin, Sara Stanley, whose mother, our Aunt Felicity, was dead, was living down on the Island with Uncle Roger and Aunt Olivia King, on a farm adjoining the old King homestead in Carlisle. We supposed we should get acquainted with her when we reached there, and we had an idea, from Aunt Olivia's letters to father, that she would be quite a jolly creature. Further than that we did not think about her. We were more interested in Felicity and Cecily and Dan, who lived on the homestead and would therefore be our roofmates for a season.

(3)   But the spirit of the Story Girl's yet unuttered remark was thrilling in our hearts that morning, as the train pulled out of Toronto. We were faring forth on a long road; and, though we had some idea what would be at the end of it, there was enough glamour of the unknown about it to lend a wonderful charm to our speculations concerning it.

(4)   We were delighted at the thought of seeing father's old home, and living among the haunts of his boyhood. He had talked so much to us about it, and described its scenes so often and so minutely, that he had inspired us with some of his own deep-seated affection for it—an affection that had never waned in all his years of exile. We had a vague feeling that we, somehow, belonged there, in that cradle of our family, though we had never seen it. We had always looked forward eagerly to the promised day when father would take us "down home," to the old house with the spruces behind it and the famous "King orchard" before it—when we might ramble in "Uncle Stephen's Walk," drink from the deep well with the Chinese roof over it, stand on "the Pulpit Stone," and eat apples from our "birthday trees."

(5)   The time had come sooner than we had dared to hope; but father could not take us after all. His firm asked him to go to Rio de Janeiro that spring to take charge of their new branch there. It was too good a chance to lose, for father was a poor man and it meant promotion and increase of salary; but it also meant the temporary breaking up of our home. Our mother had died before either of us was old enough to remember her; father could not take us to Rio de Janeiro. In the end he decided to send us to Uncle Alec and Aunt Janet down on the homestead; and our housekeeper, who belonged to the Island and was now returning to it, took charge of us on the journey. I fear she had an anxious trip of it, poor woman! She was constantly in a quite justifiable terror lest we should be lost or killed; she must have felt great relief when she reached Charlottetown and handed us over to the keeping of Uncle Alec.

It can be helpful to restate a quote or idea from a text in your own words. If a sentence or passage is very important to understanding a character, think about how you would say the same thing your own way.

Exercises

1. What is the narrator's point of view in this passage?

A. A first person narrator telling about events that have already happened.
B. A first person narrator telling about events in the present.
C. A third person narrator retelling a story told to him.
D. A third person narrator who knows the thoughts and feelings of all characters.

RL.5.6

2. What important element does the narrator introduce at the beginning of the passage?

A. The setting of the narrator's home in Toronto.
B. The fact that the narrator's mother has died.
C. Story Girl, who the narrator first knew as Sara Stanley
D. The narrator's housekeeper, who was eager to go home to Nova Scotia

RL.5.5

3. What does the housekeeper's reaction in paragraph 5 tell the reader about the boys?

A. The boys were reluctant to move to Nova Scotia
B. The boys worried that they wouldn't feel like they "belonged" in Nova Scotia
C. The boys were very active and difficult to manage during their journey from Toronto to Nova Scotia.
D. The boys were angry that their father was going to Rio de Janeiro and not to Nova Scotia with them.

RL.5.3

4. What can the reader infer from paragraph 4?

A. The boys had been to Nova Scotia before.
B. The boys' father spoke often of his home in Nova Scotia.
C. The boys' father had many photographs of his home in Nova Scotia.
D. The boys had been born in Nova Scotia and relocated to Toronto.

RL.5.1

5. What does "cradle of our family" mean as it is used in paragraph 4?

A. A crib or other structure used for infants that has been passed down for many generations.
B. A place where even older children are treated as though they were very young, and watched over carefully.
C. A place where a family began and grew into many branches of aunts and uncles and cousins.
D. A family's original home, where the children have grown up.

RL.5.4

6. What does the quote in paragraph 1 tell the reader about the character called "The Story Girl?"

A. She is adventurous and likes new experiences.
B. She is cautious and stays close to the road when she is traveling.
C. She has never been very far from home.
D. She is likely a bad influence, who may lead the boys to do things that they will regret.

RL.5.1

Columbus and the School Children *By Sidney*

(https://www.gutenberg.org/files/24904/24904-h/24904-h.htm)

(1) October, 1892, will long be remembered as the quadricentennial anniversary of America. It has been a festival month, and hardly a town or hamlet in this country but has celebrated, in some way, the landing of Columbus. New York devoted almost an entire week to land and water pageants, and Chicago, in formally dedicating the Columbian Exposition, had three days of impressive ceremonies.

(2) Two remarkable features are to be noted in connection with the October celebrations. One is, that the United States, by common consent, have monopolized the honors in connection with the discovery of this Western Continent.

(3) Of course, Columbus did not discover the United States any more than Canada. Every one knows now that he never put foot on North America at all, his nearest approach being the West India Islands, and that he did discover South America.

(4) Nevertheless it has always been recognized that here, if anywhere, rested his claims as a discoverer, and here, therefore, it was fitting that the quadricentennial should be celebrated.

(5) The second feature was the zeal with which the school children entered into the celebration. Schools, we may be assured, were little known in the days of Columbus, when monarchs thought it no shame to be unable to write their own names. Nor had Columbus any special desire to educate or civilize the people whom he found in the new lands he annexed to the Spanish crown.

(6) Yet it may be said, without exaggeration, that of all the benefits accruing to civilization that grew out of the discovery of America, not one bears any comparison with the public school system of the United States. Our forefathers were men who imbibed the love of liberty with every breath, and they early realized that liberty without intelligence was not possible, and that learning was a deadly foe to tyranny of any kind—not the learning which is confined to the few, but the learning which is free to all, without cost.

(7) There are nations, even at the present day, which designedly keep the people in ignorance, for fear that they will know their rights and demand justice. America has no such fear. Every avenue of knowledge has been opened to the child of the humblest, and in the public schools all meet on a plane of equality.

(8) So it was eminently fitting that the school children should celebrate the discovery of this new world where they are rightly considered the keystone of our national greatness. And they have celebrated it in a way such as the world has never seen.

(9) In the great civic parade in New York city on October 10, 1892 twenty-five thousand school children marched to the music of a hundred bands, before the grand-stands, on which sat the dignitaries of the nation, and to the admiring plaudits of half a million spectators who crowded the sidewalks, balconies and windows along the route.

(10) It was a sight long to be remembered, and one calculated to make the dullest thrill with love of country.

  *Ask "why" questions as you read. Why do people do certain thing? Why do people have certain feelings about a holiday? Use information from the text to answer your "why" questions.*

(11)   Later in the month, on the twenty-first, the schools all over the land, from the primary to the high schools, joined in celebrating, each in its respective schoolhouse. Speeches were made, odes sung and flags raised.

Exercises

1. What are the two key features the author associates with celebrating the quadricentennial of Columbus Day?

2. According to the text what is the most important thing that resulted from Columbus landing in the New World?

Exercises

3. What detail does the author include to demonstrate how important Columbus is to American school children?

A. He describes how America's forefathers considered education important to a free nation.
B. He describes a parade to be held in New York, with 25,000 school children and half a million spectators, commemorating Columbus and his importance to school children.
C. He describes how in some school houses, children will sing songs and give speeches.
D. He explains how Columbus's discovery is consider by some to be a "keystone of our national greatness."

RI.5.2

4. In paragraph 1, the word "hamlet" most likely refers to...

A. A nation
B. A school building
C. A parade that includes thousands of people
D. A very small town or village

RI.5.4

5. According to this passage, what role did education play in Columbus's plan when he came to the Americas?

A. One of Columbus's chief goals was to educate the people he encountered during his voyages to the Americas.
B. Columbus hoped that the nations that were established in the New World would value education as much as Spain did at the time.
C. Columbus had no interest in education and did not care if the people he encountered were educated or not.
D. Columbus feared educating people would anger the kings of Europe, many of whom could not write their own name.

RI.5.3

6. Which excerpt from the text shows that the narrator supports the idea of schoolchildren celebrating Columbus Day with such elaborate presentations?

A. So it was eminently fitting that the school children should celebrate the discovery of this new world where they are rightly considered the keystone of our national greatness.
B. In the great civic parade in New York city on October 10, 1892 twenty-five thousand school children marched to the music of a hundred bands
C. Every avenue of knowledge has been opened to the child of the humblest, and in the public schools all meet on a plane of equality.
D. Schools, we may be assured, were little known in the days of Columbus, when monarchs thought it no shame to be unable to write their own names.

RI.5.6

WEEK 18

VIDEO
EXPLANATIONS

ARGOPREP.COM

Find detailed video explanations to each problem on:
ArgoPrep.com

Fire Prevention Week *By J. Mountain*

History

(1) From October 8 to October 9 of 1871 a massive fire consumed much of the city of Chicago. More than 250 people were killed. Over 17,000 structures were burned to the ground. The Chicago fire was tremendous. But it was not the most devastating fire of the nineteenth century. It was not even the most devastating fire that week! The Peshtigo Fire struck that week in northeastern Wisconsin. It burned through sixteen towns. The conflagration destroyed over a million acres of land and buildings. Over 1100 people were killed.

(2) For many years the anniversary of these fires was commemorated with celebrations of the heroes. On the fortieth anniversary in 1911 the focus changed. The Fire Marshals Association announced it wanted to change the purpose of the day. The fire marshals decided that October 9 should be a day to remind the public of the importance of fire prevention.

(3) In 1920, President Woodrow Wilson issued a proclamation marking October 9 National Fire Prevention Day. In 1925 President Calvin Coolidge expanded the observance. He declared the week in October including the date October 9 would be National Fire Prevention Week. Every year since then, the president has issued a similar proclamation. Fire Prevention Week is observed every year in October. Every year there is a theme for the week.

Do Your Part to Prevent Fires

(4) In the first decades of National Fire Prevention Week, the themes revolved around precautions people could take at home to prevent fires in the first place. Some of these may seem common sense to modern readers. They are still important guidelines to follow. Many tips have to do with cooking. A person should stay in the kitchen whenever the stove is in use. Every year there are over 160,000 kitchen fires. They result in damage to property. They injure homeowners and firefighters. It takes just a few minutes for cooking oil to ignite. Food in a pan can quickly burn, smoke, and turn to flame. An unattended stove is a recipe for disaster.

(5) It is also important to make sure that handles of pots and pans are turned toward the back of the stove. This helps ensure they aren't bumped accidentally. When cooking, people should wear short sleeves. They should roll up longer sleeves. Loose clothing should be kept away from burners.

(6) Space heaters are another cause of fires in the home. Every year 25,000 homes catch fire because of space heaters. More than 6,000 Americans end up in emergency rooms with injuries from space heaters. Space heaters are small electrical appliances. They are used to heat single rooms. They are used in small areas. There are dangers associated with using them. According to the National Fire Protection Association, most space heater fires are caused by mistakes made by users.

Read each question carefully and make sure you note differences between answer choices that seem similar. Underline what makes the choices different.

Exercises

1. What event led eventually to establishing a day to focus on fire prevention?

   A. The Chicago Fire in 1871
   B. A proclamation from President Woodrow Wilson
   C. A proclamation from President Calvin Coolidge
   D. The start of Fire Prevention Week every October

   RI.5.1

4. Based on information in paragraph 1, the reader can determine that "conflagration" means...

   A. Mob or large group of people.
   B. Ceremony to commemorate heroes
   C. A large, uncontrolled fire
   D. An official order or event established by the government

   RI.5.4

2. What is the main idea of paragraph 6?

   A. There are more than 25,000 home fires every year.
   B. Space heaters can cause fires when used improperly.
   C. Space heaters can injure users.
   D. Space heaters are used to heat small spaces or small rooms.

   RI.5.2

5. What evidence does the author provide to show that cooking can be dangerous?

   A. A person should stay in the kitchen whenever the stove is in use.
   B. Food in a pan can quickly burn, smoke, and turn to flame.
   C. It is also important to make sure that handles of pots and pans are turned toward the back of the stove.
   D. Every year there are over 160,000 kitchen fires.

   RI.5.8

3. Which is not a cooking safety tip provided by this article?

   A. Wear short sleeves while cooking to avoid setting fire to clothing.
   B. Wear long sleeves while cooking to avoid burning arms.
   C. Turn pot handles toward the back of the stove to avoid accidentally knocking them over.
   D. Keep loose clothing away from burners on the stove.

   RI.5.3

6. Based on information in paragraph 4, what inference can the reader make about home fires?

   A. Home fires are the most deadly kind of fire.
   B. Home fires are usually caused by people who don't know basic cooking safety tips.
   C. Home fires most often start in the kitchen
   D. Most home fires start when food on the stove is left unattended.

   RI.5.1

From **Rebecca of Sunnybrook Farm** *By Kate Douglas Wiggin*

(http://www.gutenberg.org/files/498/498-h/498-h.htm)

(1) There was one passenger in the coach,—a small dark-haired person in a glossy buff calico dress. She was so slender and so stiffly starched that she slid from space to space on the leather cushions, though she braced herself against the middle seat with her feet and extended her cotton-gloved hands on each side, in order to maintain some sort of balance. Whenever the wheels sank farther than usual into a rut, or jolted suddenly over a stone, she bounded involuntarily into the air, came down again, pushed back her funny little straw hat, and picked up or settled more firmly a small pink sun shade, which seemed to be her chief responsibility,—unless we except a bead purse, into which she looked whenever the condition of the roads would permit, finding great apparent satisfaction in that its precious contents neither disappeared nor grew less. Mr. Cobb guessed nothing of these harassing details of travel, his business being to carry people to their destinations, not, necessarily, to make them comfortable on the way. Indeed he had forgotten the very existence of this one unnoteworthy little passenger.

(2) When he was about to leave the post-office in Maplewood that morning, a woman had alighted from a wagon, and coming up to him, inquired whether this were the Riverboro stage, and if he were Mr. Cobb. Being answered in the affirmative, she nodded to a child who was eagerly waiting for the answer, and who ran towards her as if she feared to be a moment too late. The child might have been ten or eleven years old perhaps, but whatever the number of her summers, she had an air of being small for her age. Her mother helped her into the stage coach, deposited a bundle and a bouquet of lilacs beside her, superintended the "roping on" behind of an old hair trunk, and finally paid the fare, counting out the silver with great care.

(3) "I want you should take her to my sisters' in Riverboro," she said. "Do you know Mirandy and Jane Sawyer? They live in the brick house."

(4) Lord bless your soul, he knew 'em as well as if he'd made 'em!

(5) "Well, she's going there, and they're expecting her. Will you keep an eye on her, please? If she can get out anywhere and get with folks, or get anybody in to keep her company, she'll do it. Good-by, Rebecca; try not to get into any mischief, and sit quiet, so you'll look neat an' nice when you get there. Don't be any trouble to Mr. Cobb.—You see, she's kind of excited.—We came on the cars from Temperance yesterday, slept all night at my cousin's, and drove from her house—eight miles it is—this morning."

(6) "Good-by, mother, don't worry; you know it isn't as if I hadn't traveled before."

(7) The woman gave a short sardonic laugh and said in an explanatory way to Mr. Cobb, "She's been to Wareham and stayed over night; that isn't much to be journey-proud on!"

(8) "It WAS TRAVELING, mother," said the child eagerly and willfully. "It was leaving the farm, and putting up lunch in a basket, and a little riding and a little steam cars, and we carried our nightgowns."

(9) "Don't tell the whole village about it, if we did," said the mother, interrupting the reminiscences of

  *A character's tone is determined by thinking about the character's words, actions, and even facial expressions. When you answer a question about tone, look for text evidence that provides these details.*

this experienced voyager. "Haven't I told you before," she whispered, in a last attempt at discipline, "that you shouldn't talk about night gowns and stockings and—things like that, in a loud tone of voice, and especially when there's men folks round?"

(10) "I know, mother, I know, and I won't. All I want to say is"—here Mr. Cobb gave a cluck, slapped the reins, and the horses started sedately on their daily task—"all I want to say is that it is a journey when"—the stage was really under way now and Rebecca had to put her head out of the window over the door in order to finish her sentence—"it IS a journey when you carry a nightgown!"

Exercises

1. Which excerpt from the text gives the reader information about the kind of little girl Rebecca is?

   A. She was so slender and so stiffly starched that she slid from space to space on the leather cushions
   B. The child might have been ten or eleven years old perhaps, but whatever the number of her summers, she had an air of being small for her age.
   C. Will you keep an eye on her, please? If she can get out anywhere and get with folks, or get anybody in to keep her company, she'll do it.
   D. "She's been to Wareham and stayed over night; that isn't much to be journey-proud on!"

   RL.5.1

2. What does the woman's tone in paragraph 7 suggest about the girls' claim that she'd traveled before?

   A. The woman believes the girl is lying about having traveled before.
   B. The woman doesn't think the girl's last trip really counts as "traveling."
   C. The woman is annoyed that the girl is talking about a trip that she should be keeping a secret.
   D. The woman is afraid the man will think less of her for allowing the child to travel alone.

   RL.5.2

3. What is the setting of this passage?

   A. A house in the country where a little girl is visiting family.
   B. A train station where a girl and her mother have arrived from a trip.
   C. A stagecoach, where a little girl is the only passenger.
   D. A post office, where a girl is meeting her mother.

   RL.5.3

4. Based on the context in paragraph 7, what is most likely the definition of "sardonic."

   A. Mocking or in a way that makes fun of someone
   B. Respectful or showing respect for someone
   C. Frightened or nervous about something that was said
   D. Resentful or having hurt feelings because of something that was said

   RL.5.4

5. What is the woman's problem with the girl, beginning in paragraph 9?

   A. The girl does not want to travel to visit her relatives.
   B. The girl mentions packing a nightgown.
   C. The girl claims she has traveled many times in the past.
   D. The girl says she wants to go home immediately.

   RL.5.5

Mother's Day *By J. Mountain*

(1)   Mother's Day is celebrated in the United States on the second Sunday in May of every year. Families around the country celebrate in many different ways. Many mothers enjoy cards, flowers, and gifts from their children. Mother's Day has a long history in the United States and in other nations around the world.

(2)   Mother's Day in America can be traced back to the work of several women. In the 1850s, Ann Reeves Jarvis of West Virginia formed clubs for mothers. She wanted to teach rural and poor mothers how to improve hygiene in their homes. She believed they could learn how to prevent diseases that killed young children. She believed they could help more children survive.

(3)   When the Civil War broke out the women in the clubs had a new mission. They wanted to help soldiers. They volunteered to care for wounded soldiers. They helped soldiers from both the north and the south. From 1861 to 1865 the women of the clubs worked in hospitals all over West Virginia.

(4)   The war ended, but many people were still angry about it. Families that supported the north were angry with families that supported the south. Jarvis worked with Julia Ward Howe to encourage mothers to help encourage peace. Together they organized Mother's Friendship Day picnics. They hoped to bring women into their organization. They wanted to teach women ways to help bring peace back to the nation.

(5)   In 1870, Howe issued the Mother's Day Proclamation. She wrote, in part, "Our sons shall not be taken from us to unlearn all that we have been able to teach them of charity, mercy, and patience." She meant that mothers taught their sons to be kind. War taught them to hate. Howe believed that mothers were authorities on peace. They knew how to help people get along. After all, Mothers had long managed disagreements in their own households. Jarvis, Howe, and others continued to use motherhood as a way to have a voice in American politics.

(6)   When Ann Jarvis died in 1904 her daughter, Anna, took up her responsibilities. Anna had different ideas about Mother's Day. Anna Jarvis was not married. She had no children. She had loved her own mother very much. Anna saw Mother's Day as a day of gratitude. She thought sons and daughters should visit their mothers and give them gifts and thanks. Anna Jarvis chose carnations to symbolize Mother's Day. Carnations were Ann Jarvis's favorite flower. Anna Jarvis established the International Mother's Day Shrine in her hometown of Grafton, West Virginia. It was important to Anna that the holiday be called Mother's Day and not Mothers' Day. To Anna, the placement of the apostrophe was very important. "Mother's Day" signified a relationship between one mother and her children. "Mothers' Day" seemed more general. It meant the day was less of a family celebration.

(7)   Anna's new vision for Mother's Day was popular with many women. Women wrote letters to leaders around the country. In 1914, President Woodrow Wilson made the day an official holiday. He proclaimed that the second Sunday in May would be observed in every state as Mother's Day. Mother's Day quickly became one of the most widely celebrated and most popular holidays in America.

    *When writing a short answer question, organize your thoughts before you write. Begin by restating the question. Always use text evidence to support the points you're making.*

Exercises

1. How did the Civil War influence people to establish Mother's Day? Use details from the text to support your answer.

RI.5.1

2. How did Anna Jarvis create enthusiasm for Mother's Day around the country?

RI.5.3

Exercises

3. What is the main idea of paragraph 6?

A. Carnations are the official flower of Mother's Day.
B. Anna Jarvis took over the responsibilities of Mother's Day because she wanted her own children to continue to carry it on.
C. Anna Jarvis took over the responsibilities of Mother's Day in honor of her mother Ann, whom she loved very much.
D. A shrine in Grafton, West Virginia was created to commemorate Mother's Day.

RI.5.2

4. What reason did Julia Ward Howe give to explain why mothers were well suited to bring peace back to the United States?

A. She believed the mothers had experience working with soldiers in during the war and would be able to help them after the war.
B. She felt that all Americans loved their mothers, so they would have some authority when they worked toward peace.
C. Mothers were experienced in solving disagreements in their own households, so they could use the same skills to solve disagreements in the nation.
D. Since everyone had a mother, everyone would understand the point of view of the women as they tried to reconcile the different sides of the Civil War.

RI.5.8

5. The writer wants to add to this text by adding the following information: Every year Americans send 141 million Mother's Day cards.

Where should the writer add this information?

A. Paragraph 1
B. Paragraph 3
C. Paragraph 4
D. Paragraph 7

RI.5.9

6. What is the meaning of the word "mission" as it is used in paragraph 3?

A. Profession
B. Job
C. Work
D. Responsibility

RI.5.4

WEEK 19

VIDEO
EXPLANATIONS

ARGOPREP.COM

From **Among the Meadow People** *By Clara Dillingham Pierson*

(http://www.gutenberg.org/files/34943/34943-h/34943-h.htm)

(1) When Mr. and Mrs. Robin built in the spring, they were not quite agreed as to where the nest should be. Mr. Robin was a very decided bird, and had made up his mind that the lowest crotch of a maple tree would be the best place. He even went so far as to take three billfuls of mud there, and stick in two blades of dry grass. Mrs. Robin wanted it on the end of the second rail from the top of the split-rail fence. She said it was high enough from the ground to be safe and dry, and not so high that a little bird falling out of it would hurt himself very much. Then, too, the top rail was broad at the end and would keep the rain off so well.

(2) "And the nest will be just the color of the rails," said she, "so that even a Red Squirrel could hardly see it." She disliked Red Squirrels, and she had reason to, for she had been married before, and if it had not been for a Red Squirrel, she might already have had children as large as she was.

(3) "I say that the tree is the place for it," said Mr. Robin, "and I wear the brightest breast feathers." He said this because in bird families the one who wears the brightest breast feathers thinks he has the right to decide things.

(4) Mrs. Robin was wise enough not to answer back when he spoke in this way. She only shook her feathers, took ten quick running steps, tilted her body forward, looked hard at the ground, and pulled out something for supper. After that she fluttered around the maple tree crotch as though she had never thought of any other place. Mr. Robin wished he had not been quite so decided, or reminded her of his breast feathers. "After all," thought he, "I don't know but the fence-rail would have done." He thought this, but he didn't say it. It is not always easy for a Robin to give up and let one with dull breast feathers know that he thinks himself wrong.

(5) That night they perched in the maple-tree and slept with their heads under their wings. Long before the sun was in sight, when the first beams were just touching the tops of the forest trees, they awakened, bright-eyed and rested, preened their feathers, sang their morning song, "Cheerily, cheerily, cheer-up," and flew off to find food. After breakfast they began to work on the nest. Mrs. Robin stopped often to look and peck at the bark. "It will take a great deal of mud," said she, "to fill in that deep crotch until we reach a place wide enough for the nest."

(6) At another time she said: "My dear, I am afraid that the dry grass you are bringing is too light-colored. It shows very plainly against the maple bark. Can't you find some that is darker?"

(7) Mr. Robin hunted and hunted, but could find nothing which was darker. As he flew past the fence, he noticed that it was almost the color of the grass in his bill.

(8) After a while, soft gray clouds began to cover the sky. "I wonder," said Mrs. Robin, "if it will rain before we get this done. The mud is soft enough now to work well, and this place is so open that the rain might easily wash away all that we have done."

  *When a character in a story changes, it doesn't always happen at the end of the story. Look for evidence throughout the story to show that the character's ideas or beliefs have changed.*

(9) It did rain, however, and very soon. The great drops came down so hard that one could only think of pebbles falling. Mr. and Mrs. Robin oiled their feathers as quickly as they could, taking the oil from their back pockets and putting it onto their feathers with their bills. This made the finest kind of waterproof and was not at all heavy to wear. When the rain was over they shook themselves and looked at their work.

(10) "I believe," said Mrs. Robin to her husband, "that you are right in saying that we might better give up this place and begin over again somewhere else."

Exercises

1. What is the reason why the birds don't build their nest on the fence?

   A. Mrs. Robin wanted to build the nest in a tree.
   B. Mr. Robin wanted to build the nest in the tree.
   C. They were afraid the squirrels would find their nest on the fence rail.
   D. The fence rail was too high and would be dangerous for baby birds.   RL.5.1

2. How does Mr. Robin change in this story?

   A. He realizes that Mrs. Robin was right about where to build the nest all along.
   B. He stops being worried about the rain.
   C. He realizes that predators like squirrels are a problem after all.
   D. He finds out that building a nest is harder than he thought it would be.   RL.5.3

3. What does the word "decided" mean as it is used in this sentence from paragraph 4?

   "Mr. Robin wished he had not been quite so decided, or reminded her of his breast feathers."

   A. Able to make a decision
   B. Able to negotiate
   C. Determined and certain
   D. Angry and overbearing   RL.5.4

4. What new problem is introduced in paragraph 9, which changes the direction of the story?

   A. Mrs. Robin sees a red squirrel moving near the new nest.
   B. Mr. Robin realizes he cannot find any grass to match the color of the bark of the maple tree.
   C. It rains and Mr. and Mrs. Robin see what the water has done to the nest.
   D. Mrs. Robin asks again if they can put up the nest on the fence.   RL.5.5

5. What is an example of the narrator sharing the thoughts or feelings of one of the characters?

   A. [Mr. Robin] even went so far as to take three billfuls of mud there, and stick in two blades of dry grass.
   B. [Mrs. Robin] only shook her feathers, took ten quick running steps, tilted her body forward, looked hard at the ground, and pulled out something for supper.
   C. When Mr. and Mrs. Robin built in the spring, they were not quite agreed as to where the nest should be.
   D. Mr. Robin wished he had not been quite so decided, or reminded her of his breast feathers.   RL.5.6

Then Laugh *by Bertha Adams Backus*

(http://100.best-poems.net/then-laugh.html)

Build for yourself a strong box,
Fashion each part with care;
When it's strong as your hand can make it,
Put all your troubles there;

Hide there all thought of your failures, (5)
And each bitter cup that you quaff;
Lock all your heartaches within it,
Then sit on the lid and laugh.

Tell no one else its contents,
Never its secrets share; (10)
When you've dropped in your care and worry
Keep them forever there;

Hide them from sight so completely
That the world will never dream half;
Fasten the strong box securely- (15)
Then sit on the lid and laugh.

Poets often use figurative language to explain feelings or emotions. As you read a poem, ask yourself if the poem is literal, meaning the poet is describing real situations, or figurative, meaning there are symbols.

Exercises

1. In which stanza does the speaker suggest that forgetting about times when you've failed can make you happier?

   A. The first stanza
   B. The second stanza
   C. The third stanza
   D. The fourth stanza

4. What is the most likely definition of the word "quaff" as it is used in line 6?

   A. Hide
   B. Lock away
   C. Drink
   D. Feel

2. What is the theme of this poem?

   A. It is important to share your hardships with others so you can overcome them.
   B. The best way to be happy is to celebrate your successes and your failures.
   C. The path to happiness is to forget all your troubles.
   D. It is better to laugh in the face of problems than to hide them away.

5. What idea is shared in the second and fourth stanzas?

   A. Other people should not be trusted.
   B. Joy is found in sharing with others.
   C. Happiness is found when things that make you feel bad are locked away.
   D. Happiness is found when people understand what makes them sad.

3. What is the speaker's opinion about secrets?

   A. They should never be shared with anyone.
   B. They should be shared with one's closest friends only.
   C. They are dangerous and keep a person from being happy.
   D. They are the key to true happiness.

6. What is the narrative point of view of this poem?

   A. First person narrative
   B. Second person narrative
   C. Third person narrative that describes only what the narrator can see.
   D. Third person narrative that describes the thoughts and feelings of others.

From **20,000 Leagues Under the Sea** *by Jules Verne*

(http://www.gutenberg.org/files/2488/2488-h/2488-h.htm)

(1)   The Canadian paused in his work. But one word twenty times repeated, one dreadful word, told me the reason for the agitation spreading aboard the Nautilus. We weren't the cause of the crew's concern.

(2)   "Maelstrom! Maelstrom!" they were shouting.

(3)   The Maelstrom! Could a more frightening name have rung in our ears under more frightening circumstances? Were we lying in the dangerous waterways off the Norwegian coast? Was the Nautilus being dragged into this whirlpool just as the skiff was about to detach from its plating?

(4)   As you know, at the turn of the tide, the waters confined between the Varrö and Lofoten Islands rush out with irresistible violence. They form a vortex from which no ship has ever been able to escape. Monstrous waves race together from every point of the horizon. They form a whirlpool aptly called "the ocean's navel," whose attracting power extends a distance of fifteen kilometers. It can suck down not only ships but whales, and even polar bears from the northernmost regions.

(5)   This was where the Nautilus had been sent accidentally—or perhaps deliberately—by its captain. It was sweeping around in a spiral whose radius kept growing smaller and smaller. The skiff, still attached to the ship's plating, was likewise carried around at dizzying speed. I could feel us whirling. I was experiencing that accompanying nausea that follows such continuous spinning motions. We were in dread, in the last stages of sheer horror, our blood frozen in our veins, our nerves numb, drenched in cold sweat as if from the throes of dying! And what a noise around our frail skiff! What roars echoing from several miles away! What crashes from the waters breaking against sharp rocks on the sea floor, where the hardest objects are smashed, where tree trunks are worn down and worked into "a shaggy fur," as Norwegians express it!

(6)   What a predicament! We were rocking frightfully. The Nautilus defended itself like a human being. Its steel muscles were cracking. Sometimes it stood on end, the three of us along with it!

(7)   "We've got to hold on tight," Ned said, "and screw the nuts down again! If we can stay attached to the Nautilus, we can still make it … !"

(8)   He hadn't finished speaking when a cracking sound occurred. The nuts gave way, and ripped out of its socket, the skiff was hurled like a stone from a sling into the midst of the vortex.

(9)   My head struck against an iron timber, and with this violent shock I lost consciousness.

If you're stuck on a question, don't give up. Eliminate answer choices that are definitely incorrect, and check the remaining by going back to the text to see if you can find evidence to support the response.

Exercises

1. What does the narrator believe, at first, is the reason why the crew is so upset?

2. What problem are the characters in this passage facing?

Exercises

3. Which statement best supports the conclusion that the narrator is in a smaller boat attached to the Nautilus?

A. "We've got to hold on tight," Ned said.
B. "We were in dread, in the last stages of sheer horror, our blood frozen in our veins, our nerves numb, drenched in cold sweat..."
C. "What a predicament! We were rocking frightfully!"
D. "The skiff, still attached to the ship's plating, was likewise carried around at dizzying speed. I could feel us whirling."

RL.5.1

5. What assumption does the narrator make in paragraph 4?

A. The narrator assumes the reader knows how the story ends.
B. The narrator assumes the reader is familiar with common words from a language other than English.
C. The narrator assumes the reader is familiar with a specific area in the sea, between two islands.
D. The narrator assumes that the reader has gone through a similar experience.

RL.5.6

4. What is the best synonym for "deliberately" as it is used in paragraph 5?

A. Purposely
B. Accidentally
C. Impulsively
D. Oddly

RL.5.4

6. Review this sentence from paragraph 8. What is the simile excerpt?

"He hadn't finished speaking when a cracking sound occurred. The nuts gave way, and ripped out of its socket, the skiff was hurled like a stone from a sling into the midst of the vortex."

A. He hadn't finished speaking
B. The nuts gave way...
C. ...when a cracking sound occurred.
D. The skiff was hurled like a stone...

RL.5.4

WEEK 20

VIDEO
EXPLANATIONS

ARGOPREP.COM

Song of Wandering Aengus *by William Butler Yeats*

(https://www.poetryfoundation.org/poems-and-poets/poems/detail/55687)

I went out to the hazel wood,
Because a fire was in my head,
And cut and peeled a hazel wand,
And hooked a berry to a thread;
And when white moths were on the wing,   (5)
And moth-like stars were flickering out,
I dropped the berry in a stream
And caught a little silver trout.

When I had laid it on the floor
I went to blow the fire a-flame,   (10)
But something rustled on the floor,
And someone called me by my name:
It had become a glimmering girl
With apple blossom in her hair
Who called me by my name and ran   (15)
And faded through the brightening air.

Though I am old with wandering
Through hollow lands and hilly lands,
I will find out where she has gone,
And kiss her lips and take her hands;   (20)
And walk among long dappled grass,
And pluck till time and times are done,
The silver apples of the moon,
The golden apples of the sun.   (24)

Take notice of the verbs used in a text – are they past tense, indicating they describe something that happened earlier? Present tense? Future? The verb tense gives you important information about the narrator.

Exercises

1. Based on the clues in the first stanza, a hazel is most likely...

   A. A kind of tree
   B. A type of fish
   C. A woman's name
   D. A type of cloth

   RL.5.4

4. What transformation occurs in the second stanza of the poem?

   A. The wand transforms into a fish
   B. The berries transform into a woman
   C. The fish transforms into a woman
   D. The man transforms into a magical creature

   RL.5.5

2. The narrative point of view of this poem is...

   A. A young man describing his first love.
   B. An old man describing something that happened in the past.
   C. A third person narrator retelling a story that has been passed down to him.
   D. A second person narrator giving the reader advice.

   RL.5.6

5. How does seeing the beautiful girl with the flowers in her hair change the speaker of the poem?

   A. He dedicates his life to finding her again
   B. He decides that he does believe in magic
   C. He gives up trying to find happiness and love.
   D. He spends the rest of his life at the stream, looking for another magic trout.

   RL.5.3

3. The theme of this poem is ...

   A. The power of magic
   B. The importance of pursuing your dreams
   C. The heartbreak of losing something you love
   D. How loneliness leads to imagining things

   RL.5.2

6. What is missing from the end of the poem?

   A. Information about the setting
   B. The resolution or if the speaker ever finds the girl.
   C. An explanation for how the girl was created.
   D. Information about the man who is the main character in the poem.

   RL.5.5

From **Little Women** *By Louisa May Alcott*

(http://www.gutenberg.org/files/514/514-h/514-h.htm)

(1) For a year Jo and her Professor worked and waited, hoped and loved, met occasionally, and wrote such voluminous letters that the rise in the price of paper was accounted for, Laurie said. The second year began rather soberly, for their prospects did not brighten, and Aunt March died suddenly. But when their first sorrow was over—for they loved the old lady in spite of her sharp tongue—they found they had cause for rejoicing, for she had left Plumfield to Jo, which made all sorts of joyful things possible.

(2) "It's a fine old place, and will bring a handsome sum, for of course you intend to sell it," said Laurie, as they were all talking the matter over some weeks later.

(3) "No, I don't," was Jo's decided answer, as she petted the fat poodle, whom she had adopted, out of respect to his former mistress.

(4) "You don't mean to live there?"

(5) "Yes, I do."

(6) "But, my dear girl, it's an immense house, and will take a power of money to keep it in order. The garden and orchard alone need two or three men, and farming isn't in Bhaer's line, I take it."

(7) "He'll try his hand at it there, if I propose it."

(8) "And you expect to live on the produce of the place? Well, that sounds paradisiacal, but you'll find it desperate hard work."

(9) "The crop we are going to raise is a profitable one," and Jo laughed.

(10) "Of what is this fine crop to consist, ma'am?"

(11) "Boys. I want to open a school for little lads—a good, happy, homelike school, with me to take care of them and Fritz to teach them."

(12) "That's a truly Joian plan for you! Isn't that just like her?" cried Laurie, appealing to the family, who looked as much surprised as he.

(13) "I like it," said Mrs. March decidedly.

(14) "So do I," added her husband, who welcomed the thought of a chance for trying the Socratic method of education on modern youth.

(15) "It will be an immense care for Jo," said Meg, stroking the head of her one all-absorbing son.

(16) "Jo can do it, and be happy in it. It's a splendid idea. Tell us all about it," cried Mr. Laurence, who had been longing to lend the lovers a hand, but knew that they would refuse his help.

When a passage has many characters the most important characters are usually those who are facing a challenge or have to make a decision.

(17)   "I knew you'd stand by me, sir. Amy does too—I see it in her eyes, though she prudently waits to turn it over in her mind before she speaks. Now, my dear people," continued Jo earnestly, "just understand that this isn't a new idea of mine, but a long cherished plan. Before my Fritz came, I used to think how, when I'd made my fortune, and no one needed me at home, I'd hire a big house, and pick up some poor, forlorn little lads who hadn't any mothers, and take care of them, and make life jolly for them before it was too late. I see so many going to ruin for want of help at the right minute, I love so to do anything for them, I seem to feel their wants, and sympathize with their troubles, and oh, I should so like to be a mother to them!"

(18)   Mrs. March held out her hand to Jo, who took it, smiling, with tears in her eyes, and went on in the old enthusiastic way, which they had not seen for a long while.

Exercises

1. Why does Laurie try at first to convince Jo to sell the house she's inherited?

   A. Because it would be too expensive to keep it.
   B. Jo and her husband are not experienced farmers.
   C. Jo has no children of her own to fill such a big house.
   D. Jo and her husband need the money that they would get from selling the house.   RL.5.1

2. How is Meg's response to Jo's plan different from Mrs. March's response?

   A. Meg thinks the plan will be a great deal of work, while Mrs. March believes it is a wonderful plan.
   B. Meg thinks the plan is a very good idea, but Mrs. March doesn't think it is practical.
   C. Meg doesn't think Jo and her husband will be able to go through with the plan, but Mrs. March thinks Jo's husband will lead them to success.
   D. Mrs. March thinks Jo would be better off getting the money and pursuing her dream in a different way, but Meg believes Jo should keep the house in the family.

   RL.5.3

3. Review this excerpt from paragraph 17; what is the most likely meaning of the phrase "long cherished?"

   "...just understand that this isn't a new idea of mine, but a long cherished plan."

   A. Something that has been a secret for a long time
   B. Something she has had and held onto for a very long time
   C. Something that is worth a lot of money or has great value
   D. Something that no one else understands   RL.5.4

4. How would the passage have been different if it had been told from the point of view of Jo?

   A. The story would have begun with more detail about Jo and the professor and what they did prior to inheriting the house.
   B. There would not have been a discussion of what Jo should do with the house.
   C. The reader would have known from the beginning of the passage what Jo planned to do with the house.
   D. The reader would have learned more about "Jo's Professor" and what he wanted to do in the house.

   RL.5.6

Banks From Principles of Economics

Download for free at http://cnx.org/contents/69619d2b-68f0-44b0-b074-a9b2bf90b2c6@11.333.

(1) The late bank robber named Willie Sutton was once asked why he robbed banks. He answered: "That's where the money is." While this may have been true at one time, from the perspective of modern economists, Sutton is both right and wrong. He is wrong because the overwhelming majority of money in the economy is not in the form of currency sitting in vaults or drawers at banks, waiting for a robber to appear. Most money is in the form of bank accounts, which exist only as electronic records on computers. From a broader perspective, however, the bank robber was more right than he may have known. Banking is interconnected with money and with the broader economy.

(2) Banks make it far easier for a complex economy to carry out the extraordinary range of transactions that occur in goods, labor, and financial capital markets. Imagine for a moment what the economy would be like if all payments had to be made in cash. When shopping for a large purchase or going on vacation you might need to carry hundreds of dollars in a pocket or purse. Even small businesses would need stockpiles of cash to pay workers and to purchase supplies. A bank allows people and businesses to store this money in either a checking account or savings account, for example, and then withdraw this money as needed through the use of a direct withdrawal, writing a check, or using a debit card.

(3) Banks are a critical intermediary in what is called the payment system, which helps an economy exchange goods and services for money or other financial assets. Also, those with extra money that they would like to save can store their money in a bank rather than look for an individual that is willing to borrow it from them and then repay them at a later date. Those who want to borrow money can go directly to a bank rather than trying to find someone to lend them cash Transaction costs are the costs associated with finding a lender or a borrower for this money. Thus, banks lower transactions costs and act as financial intermediaries—they bring savers and borrowers together. Along with making transactions much safer and easier, banks also play a key role in the creation of money.

(4) An "intermediary" is one who stands between two other parties. Banks are a financial intermediary—that is, an institution that operates between a saver who deposits money in a bank and a borrower who receives a loan from that bank. Financial intermediaries include other institutions in the financial market such as insurance companies and pension funds, but they will not be included in this discussion because they are not considered to be depository institutions, which are institutions that accept money deposits and then use these to make loans. All the funds deposited are mingled in one big pool, which is then loaned out.

Never turn in a written response until you've proofread it carefully. Errors can interfere with the meaning of your response and keep you from getting the highest grade.

Exercises

1. What was the author's purpose in writing this text?

RI.5.1

2. Why does the author begin the passage by quoting a bank robber?

RI.5.8

3. What is the meaning of "intermediary" as it is used in this text?

A. Bank or other financial institution.
B. Any institution that makes loans.
C. A go-between or something that makes a connection between two other things.
D. A store that receives payments electronically.

RI.5.4

5. What is the main idea of paragraph 3?

A. Banks store money for people who have extra and loan money to people who need more.
B. Banks make money when people put money in their savings accounts.
C. Banks can only loan as much money as people have put into savings accounts.
D. Since it is difficult to find lenders, banks help people who need money connect with people who have extra money.

RI.5.2

4. How is information in paragraph 2 organized?

A. Cause and effect
B. Chronologically
C. Problem and solution
D. Definition and explanation

RI.5.5

6. Based on information in the passage, what is the best definition of the word "transaction" as it is used in the passage?

A. A conversation that ends with an agreement.
B. Exchanging money when something is bought or sold.
C. Opening and managing a business.
D. Any activity that involves two or more people

RI.5.4

ANSWER
KEYS

VIDEO
EXPLANATIONS

ARGOPREP.COM

WEEK 1

Monday
1: B
2: B
3: C
4: A
5: C
6: B

Tuesday
1: C
2: A
3: C
4: B
5: D
6: C

Friday
1: Perspiring requires less energy, so it does not tire the human to perspire.
2: With the invention of projectile weapons hunters could kill their prey from a distance, and did not need to chase it; it made it less important that humans be strong runners.
3: B
4: A
5: A
6: C

WEEK 2

Monday
1: C
2: D
3: C
4: A
5: D
6: B

Wednesday
1: A
2: B
3: D
4: C

5: C
6: C

Friday
1: Washington grew up poor with few educational opportunities but still grew to become a respected professional and solider. During the difficult times of war, he rose to the occasion and became a great leader.
2: Washington was respected because of the seriousness of his character, as well as his physical and mental strength.
3: B
4: D
5: C
6: B

WEEK 3

Monday
1: B
2: C
3: D
4: C
5: A
6: C

Wednesday
1: C
2: B
3: A
4: B
5: C
6: C

Friday
1: The sister thought the name was funny because she believed the general was named after their pony and not the other way around.
2: The father is described as "wholeheartedly performing every

duty," enjoying to entertain guests, and charitable when it came to helping others.
3: C
4: D
5: A
6: C

WEEK 4

Monday
1: D
2: D
3: A
4: B
5: C
6: D

Wednesday
1: C
2: D
3: D
4: B
5: C
6: A

Friday
1: Dr. Doolittle does not care what the "best people" think at all, and prefers to focus on his passion for animals rather than making money practicing human medicine.
2: The reader can tell Sarah is frustrated with her brother because she calls him "ridiculous" and tells him that he is hurting his business by focusing on animals and not paying human customers.
3: B
4: D
5: A
6: C

WEEK 5

Monday

1: B
2: B
3: D
4: D
5: A

Wednesday

1: B
2: D
3: A
4: B
5: C
6: D

Friday

1: Technology includes innovations and inventions from all different eras, including stone tools, the earliest computers, the first calculator, and all the way up to modern DNA technology.
2: Social media has empowered people to make changes their societies. For example, a girl created a petition to Hasbro to make a gender-neutral Easy-Bake Oven and people in Latvia created a petition platform so the citizens could sign petitions and get the government's attention on important issues.
3: D
4: B
5: A
6: C

WEEK 6

Monday

1: B
2: C
3: A
4: B
5: A
6: D

Wednesday

1: B
2: D
3: D
4: B
5: A

Friday

1: He recalls that his father called her that, and he learned to do so from his father. He sees that she has been ill, and is just starting to feel better, and he wants to comfort her.
2: In paragraph 6 Cedric learns that he and his mother are alone now that his father has died. His mother says that his father is "well," meaning he is no longer sick. But he has not recovered, he has passed away, leaving them on their own.
3: B
4: A
5:
6: A

WEEK 7

Monday

1: D
2: C
3: C
4: B

Wednesday

1: B
2: C
3: B
4: C
5: A
6: C

Friday

1: In the past shoe makers traveled from farm to farm with their tools and made complete pairs of shoes. Now shoes are made from different components, each of which is made in a factory.
2: According to the text, one reason it can be difficult to find a shoe that fits well is that, 'Your feet are not exactly like those of any one else.' In addition, shoes must be very durable, as well as comfortable because, "shoes have harder wear than anything else in one's wardrobe."
3: C
4: D
5: D
6: A

WEEK 8

Monday

1: B
2: B
3: A
4: C

Wednesday

1: B
2: B
3: A
4: B

Friday

1: The value of the White Mountains as a tourist destination is much greater than the value of the timber that grows in its forests.
2: To persuade readers that the forests of the White Mountains should not be cut down.
3: C
4: C
5: D
6: B

WEEK 9

Monday

1: C
2: A
3: B
4: D
5: C

6: A

Wednesday

1: D
2: B
3: D
4: B

Friday

1: They were nearly self-sufficient, and the farmer's wives spent very little money, less than twelve dollars a year, to create all the blankets, towels, clothing they needed. She thought they were frugal and very respectable because they worked so hard.
2: Women in the city work very hard for wages, rather than working hard on their family farms. This is ironic because their labor or their work is for the same reasons – they work so that they can have fine things. Instead of creating their own clothing, women in the cities work in factories all day, then buy clothing.
3: A
4: D
5: B
6: C

WEEK 10

Monday

1: C
2: C
3: D
4: A
5: B
6: D

Wednesday

1: B
2: C
3: C
4: B
5: D
6: A

Friday

1: The children are laughing because Mrs. Viney thinks their mother is being very economical with her coal. The truth is that there is considerably more coal in the cellar because Peter, with help from the other children, has stolen coal to bring to their house.
2: It is likely that the children's family was once wealthier than it is now. At the beginning of the story the narrator notes that the children wore the "same kind of nice clothes" they'd worn before, and that there was always enough to eat. However, it becomes clear by paragraph 7 that the family is cutting back on expenses and cannot keep their home as warm as they once could
3: A
4: B
5: C
6: C

WEEK 11

Monday

1: B
2: C
3: D
4: B
5: C
6: B

Wednesday

1: D
2: B
3: B
4: B
5: C
6: A

Friday

1: The secret garden was a neglected garden near Mary's home. It was surrounded by walls, so Mary felt hidden when she was in there. It had not been tended in a long time, about ten years, so it there were many weeds and neglected plants for Mary to take care of.
2: Mary initially treated Weatherstaff rudely, as a servant, and spoke to him only to give him commands. She didn't know that she was in a new environment, and that she should be respectful toward him. Mary enjoyed Weatherstaff's company, so she was respectful and quiet when she approached him, so he would not walk away from her.
3: A
4: B
5: C
6: A

WEEK 12

Monday

1: A
2: C
3: C
4: B
5: D
6: A

Wednesday

1: A
2: C
3: B
4: C
5: C
6: B

Friday

1: B
2: A
3: C
4: C
5: The author compares the nervous system to a telephone system to help the reader understand that messages are transmitted via nerves or wires to the brain. The brain is

compared to a central telephone office where all messages pass through. The nerves are referred to as "cords" or wires, that lead to and from the central office.

6: The author attempted to simplify complex ideas into terms that a younger reader could understand. The author provided examples that are familiar to a young reader, such as burning her finger on a hot stove," and referred to expressions that might be familiar, such as "as quick as a thought" to explain how nerves communicate with the brain.

WEEK 13

Monday

1: C
2: B
3: D
4: C
5: D
6: B

Wednesday

1: B
2: C
3: D
4: B
5: B
6: C

Friday

1: The phoenix is grateful to Robert for putting his egg in the faire and says to the boy, "I am your grateful debtor." Now that he is brought back, the bird is very curious about what people think of him. He asks if there are any portraits of him and wants to hear the description of him from the book Robert has.

2: The phoenix definitely knows who he is, but he wants to hear what others have written about him, and through his comments about what

was written, he shares more about himself. For example, when Robert reads that the phoenix is a "bird of antiquity" meaning that it is very old, he agrees, but he asks the children if they agree that he is "fabulous" or very beautiful. He is building his impression of himself through these comments.

3: A
4: B
5: C
6: B

WEEK 14

Monday

1: C
2: B
3: A
4: C
5: C
6: C

Wednesday

1: A
2: D
3: D
4: B
5: C
6: C

Friday

1: To amuse readers with a story about an old man who does surprising things. He also wanted to show that a man's life experiences make him stronger. For example, because he had to exercise his jaw by arguing with his wife, Father William was able to chew food when he was an old man. Even though he was discouraged from standing on his head as a young man, because it might hurt his brain, he's still able to do so, and doesn't bother worrying about hurting himself any more.

2: He's tired of them. He believes

he's been patient in answering three questions, but he refuses to answer any more. He even threatens to kick his son down the stairs if he asks him anything else.

3: B
4: C
5: -
6: "Do you think I can listen all day to such stuff? Be off, or I'll kick you downstairs!" In these lines, William is showing that he is frustrated by, first, suggesting that he doesn't have all day to listen to these silly questions. Then, to prove his point, he threatens to kick the young man if he asks one more question. These two statements show that William has grown impatient with the questioning and wants it to end.

WEEK 15

Monday

1: A
2: C
3: A
4: B
5: D
6: B

Wednesday

1: B
2: C
3: A
4: C
5: C
6: A

Friday

1: People who earn more money may spend time thinking about money in a way that interferes with their ability to enjoy simple pleasures, such as the taste of chocolate or other everyday experiences. Not being able to enjoy small pleasures makes people less happy overall.

2: In an experiment, some people were reminded of wealth with subtle hints while they were eating a chocolate bar. The people who were constantly reminded about wealth enjoyed the candy bar less than the people who were not reminded.
3: C
4: B
5: A
6: D

WEEK 16

Monday

1: C
2: A
3: C
4: C
5: D
6: A

Wednesday

1: B
2: C
3: C
4: D
5: D
6: D

Friday

1: Sara says that "she did not know all that being rich meant." Which means she did not understand the concept of being rich. She was a child and only knew what her own life was like. She did not have anything to compare it to, and, could not judge if she lived a life that was richer than that of other people.
2: In paragraph 10, the narrator says that Sara knows that she and her father will "have to be apart for some time." Since they have reached "the place," and have traveled from India to London together, it is likely that this is where they will be separated. Sara's papa is very fond of her, and it

no doubt makes him sad that he will have to leave her somewhere for a period of time.
3: D
4: C
5: A
6: C

WEEK 17

Monday

1: B
2: A
3: C
4: C
5: A
6: B

Wednesday

1: A
2: C
3: C
4: B
5: C
6: A

Friday

1: The first feature is that the United States seems to have "monopolized the honors" in celebrating Columbus's discovering of the Western Continent, even though he did not actually discover the United States. The second feature is that the celebration is particularly important to children and celebrated to a great degree in schools.
2: This author claims that "of all the benefits...that grew out of the discovery of America" the greatest is the public school system of the United States. The author says that in the United States all people have the right to an education, which is different from other countries, and that in the United States, it does not matter if a person is rich or poor or lives in the city or country, he will

still be given an education.
3: B
4: D
5: C
6: A

WEEK 18

Monday

1: A
2: B
3: B
4: C
5: D
6: C

Wednesday

1: C
2: B
3: C
4: A
5: B

Friday

1: During the Civil War, a women's club created to teach poor mothers how to improve hygiene in their homes turned their attention to helping wounded soldiers. They worked in hospitals in West Virginia from 1861 to 1865. After the war the women hoped to bring people together to get over the anger people felt about the war.
2: She inspired many women to support the holiday and they wrote letters to government leaders. Finally in 1914 President Wilson made Mother's Day an official holiday.
3: C
4: C
5: A
6: D

WEEK 19

Monday

1: B
2: A
3: C
4: C
5: D

Wednesday

1: B
2: C
3: A
4: C
5: C
6: B

Friday

1: At the beginning of the passage the narrator listens to the crew repeating one word, and eventually he realizes that he and his group are not the "cause of the crew's concern." They are, in fact, upset about a "Maelstrom" they've spotted on the water.

2: They are approaching a whirlpool in the water, a vortex, that threatens to pull the ship underwater. The location of the vortex is well known, so the narrator is concerned that the ship's captain has brought them there on purpose.

3: D
4: A
5: C
6: D

WEEK 20

Monday

1: A
2: B
3: C
4: C
5: A
6: B

Wednesday

1: B

2: A
3: B
4: C

Friday

1: The author wrote this text to explain the role of banks in the economy and commerce. The author explains how banks move and manage money so that the economy can operate.

2: The author begins the passage by quoting Willie Sutton to point out that banks don't actually hold a lot of physical currency. The purpose of the passage is to explain how money is transferred electronically from one account to another, and does not physically change hands.

3: C
4: C
5: A
6: B

Made in the USA
Middletown, DE
27 July 2017